DISSECTION GUIDE
FOR
THE CAT

(and Selected Sheep Organs)

by
Kenneth G. Neal
Barbara H. Kalbus
Long Beach City College
Long Beach, California

Burgess Publishing Company
• Minneapolis, Minn.

Preface

This dissection guide has been designed to supplement laboratory manuals or materials which may be acceptable for a particular course in most respects, but which may be deficient in providing adequate guidance in the dissection of the cat.

Included are procedures for dissecting the sheep eye, brain, and heart. These materials are readily available and are frequently used for the sake of convenience. The size of each of these organs in relation to those of the cat may make these more desirable to dissect.

The authors would like to express their appreciation for the illustrations drawn by Joan Van Moorlehem, Diana Jacobson, and Robert Bush.

Kenneth G. Neal

Barbara H. Kalbus

Contents

The External Anatomy of the Cat

The cat, <u>Felis</u> <u>domestica</u>, is frequently dissected in classes in human anatomy, since it has many features which are similar to humans (both belong to the class Mammalia). As the cat is dissected and studied throughout the course, the structures identified should be compared with those of the human.

The terms <u>right</u> and <u>left</u> always refer to the cat's right and left. In a quadruped, <u>anterior</u> or <u>cranial</u> refers to the head end; <u>posterior</u> or <u>caudal</u> to the tail end; <u>dorsal</u> or <u>superior</u> to the back; <u>ventral</u> or <u>inferior</u> to the belly. <u>Lateral</u> refers to the side; <u>medial</u> to the position of a structure nearer the midline of the body (see Figure 1). The drawings provided will serve as a guide to your dissection. However, it should be noted that there may be some variation among cats, particularly in the circulatory system.

Dissection is not merely "cutting" the animal, but is a systematic technique of bringing into view structures which, in their normal position, cannot readily be seen. Do not cut or remove any structure unless directed to do so. Never cut a structure before knowing what it is. Always separate structures carefully, especially muscles and blood vessels, by dissecting away connective tissue. Use a dissecting needle rather than a scalpel wherever possible.

You may find that the substances used to preserve the specimen are irritating to your skin. If so, apply "pro-tek" (or some similar substance) to your hands before dissecting, or wear thin rubber or plastic gloves. Keep your fingers away from your eyes during dissection.

At the conclusion of each laboratory period, clean up the working area thoroughly. Wrap the cat in wet paper towels and replace it in the plastic bag provided. Place a rubber band over the end of the plastic bag. Do not leave any solid material in the sink. Clean and dry the laboratory table and your dissecting instruments.

PROCEDURE

1.   Observe the following external features in the cat: head, neck, thorax, abdomen, and tail. Determine the number of pairs of nipples on the ·trunk. Observe whether the nipples are located on both the male and the female cat.

2.   Observe the forelegs and hindlegs of the cat. The foreleg consists of the arm (<u>brachium</u>), the forearm (<u>antebrachium</u>), the wrist, palm, and digits. The hindleg consists of the thigh, shank, foot, and digits. Determine the number of digits on both the foreleg and hindleg.

3.   Observe the retractable claws. Locate the friction pads (<u>tori</u>) on the bottom of the paws.

4.   Examine the skeleton of the cat. Note that the cat walks on its toes (digitigrade method of locomotion) rather than on the soles of the feet (plantigrade method of locomotion).

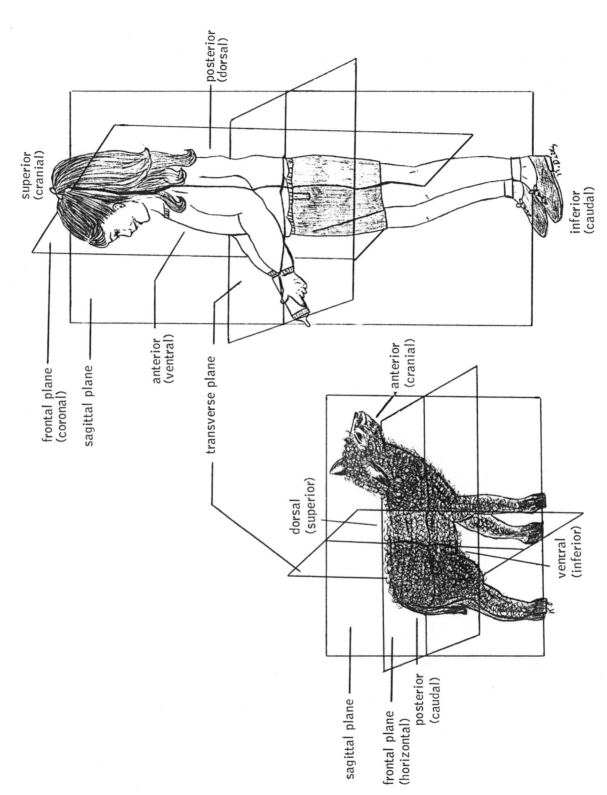

Figure 1. Planes of the Body

5. On the head, locate the tactile whiskers (vibrissae) around the mouth; the external nares; the auricle (or pinna), which is part of the external ear; and the eyelids (palpebrae). Spread the eyelids apart and locate the thin nictitating membrane in the medial corner of the eye. This membrane extends laterally over the eyeball, keeping it moist.

6. Determine the sex of your specimen. In both sexes the anus, the opening of the rectum to the outside, is found ventral to the tail. In the male, the scrotum, which contains the testes, is located anterior to the anus. In the female, the urogenital aperture is also located just anterior to the anus.

The Skeletal System

The skeletal system of the cat is similar to that of the human. Some of the major differences between the skeleton of the cat and of man are as follows:

1. There are seven cervical, thirteen thoracic, seven lumbar vertebrae, one sacrum (three sacral vertebrae united into one bone), and approximately twenty-one to twenty-three caudal vertebrae in the cat.

2. There are thirteen pairs of ribs in the cat.

3. There are six sternebrae in the body of the sternum in the cat.

4. There are seven carpal bones in the wrist of the cat instead of eight.

5. There are only four digits on the foot of the cat hindleg.

6. There are additional bones in the skull of the cat such as two premaxillary bones, one interparietal bone, two frontal bones instead of one; the sphenoid bone is divided into three parts (the presphenoid, the basisphenoid, and the alisphenoid).

7. The clavicles are much reduced in size in the cat and do not articulate with the sternum. They are embedded in muscles of the shoulder.

8. The hyoid in the cat consists of a chain of ossicles in the throat instead of a single bone. It supports the base of the tongue.

You will also note a variation in the shape of some of the bones.

PROCEDURE

1. Study the articulated cat skeleton (Figure 2). Except for the skull, locate each of the bones of the appendicular and axial skeleton.

2. Study the cat skull (Figures 3-5). Locate each of the bones, sutures, and major processes.

3. Next identify each of the bones of the disarticulated cat skeleton. Locate the processes identified in Figures 6-12.

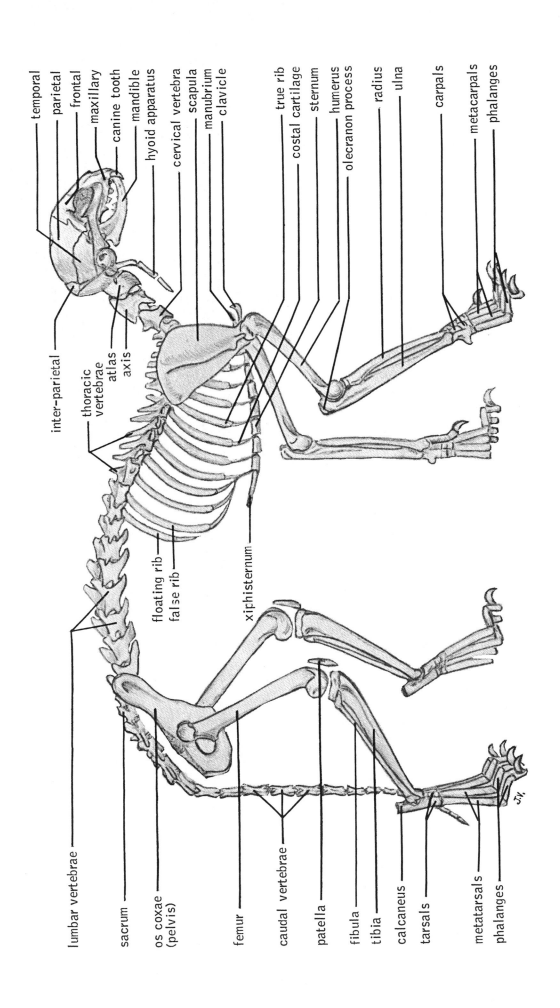

Figure 2: Lateral View of the Cat Skeleton

temporal
parietal
frontal
maxillary
canine tooth
mandible
hyoid apparatus
cervical vertebra
scapula
manubrium
clavicle
true rib
costal cartilage
sternum
humerus
olecranon process
radius
ulna
carpals
metacarpals
phalanges

inter-parietal
thoracic vertebrae
atlas
axis

floating rib
false rib

xiphisternum

lumbar vertebrae
sacrum
os coxae (pelvis)
femur
caudal vertebrae
patella
fibula
tibia
calcaneus
tarsals
metatarsals
phalanges

5

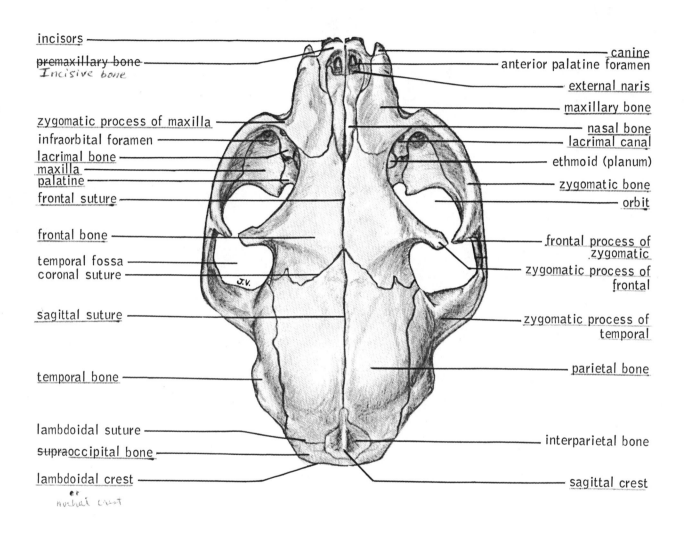

incisors

premaxillary bone
Incisive bone

zygomatic process of maxilla
infraorbital foramen
lacrimal bone
maxilla
palatine
frontal suture

frontal bone

temporal fossa
coronal suture

sagittal suture

temporal bone

lambdoidal suture
supraoccipital bone

lambdoidal crest
nuchal crest

canine
anterior palatine foramen
external naris
maxillary bone
nasal bone
lacrimal canal
ethmoid (planum)
zygomatic bone
orbit

frontal process of zygomatic
zygomatic process of frontal

zygomatic process of temporal

parietal bone

interparietal bone

sagittal crest

J.V.

Figure 3: Dorsal View of Skull

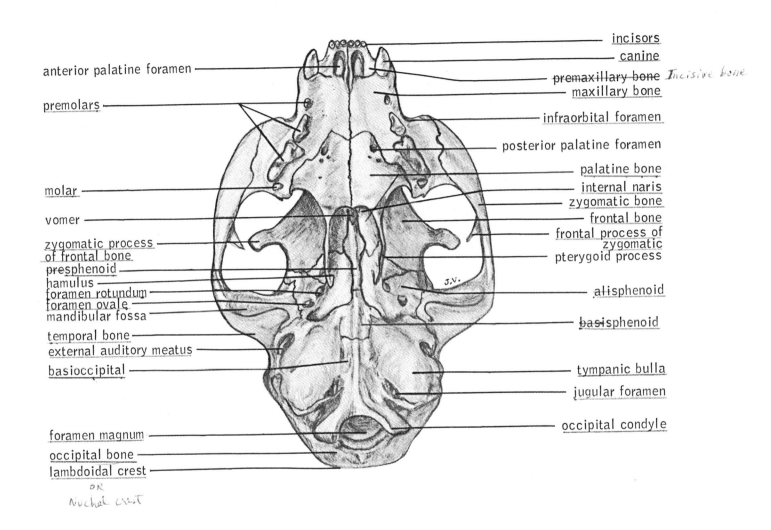

incisors

canine

premaxillary bone *Incisive bone*

maxillary bone

infraorbital foramen

posterior palatine foramen

palatine bone

internal naris

zygomatic bone

frontal bone

frontal process of zygomatic

pterygoid process

alisphenoid

basisphenoid

tympanic bulla

jugular foramen

occipital condyle

anterior palatine foramen

premolars

molar

vomer

zygomatic process of frontal bone

presphenoid

hamulus

foramen rotundum

foramen ovale

mandibular fossa

temporal bone

external auditory meatus

basioccipital

foramen magnum

occipital bone

lambdoidal crest

OR

Nuchal crest

J.V.

Figure 4: Skull of Cat, Ventral View

7

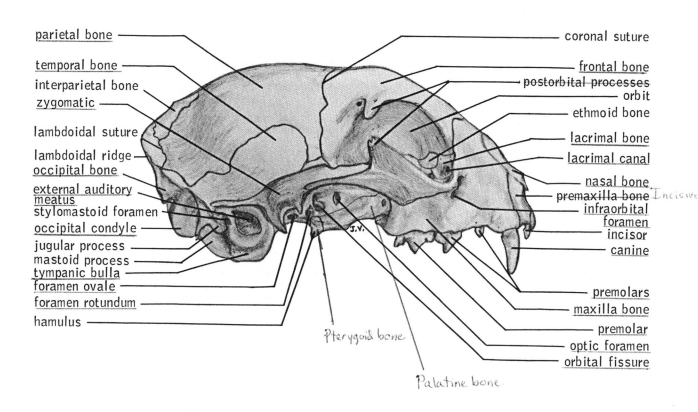

parietal bone — coronal suture

temporal bone — frontal bone
interparietal bone — postorbital processes
zygomatic — orbit
— ethmoid bone
lambdoidal suture — lacrimal bone
lambdoidal ridge — lacrimal canal
occipital bone — nasal bone
external auditory meatus — premaxilla bone   Incisive b
stylomastoid foramen — infraorbital foramen
occipital condyle — incisor
jugular process — canine
mastoid process
tympanic bulla
foramen ovale — premolars
foramen rotundum — maxilla bone
hamulus — premolar
Pterygoid bone — optic foramen
— orbital fissure
Palatine bone

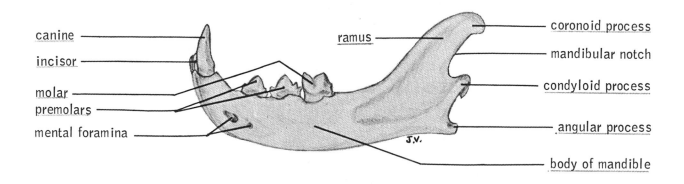

canine — coronoid process
incisor — mandibular notch
molar — condyloid process
premolars — angular process
mental foramina — body of mandible

ramus

Figure 5: Lateral View of Skull and Mandible

Atlas - Ventral View

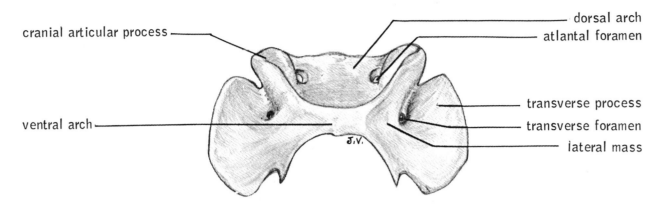

cranial articular process

ventral arch

dorsal arch

atlantal foramen

transverse process

transverse foramen

lateral mass

Axis - Lateral View

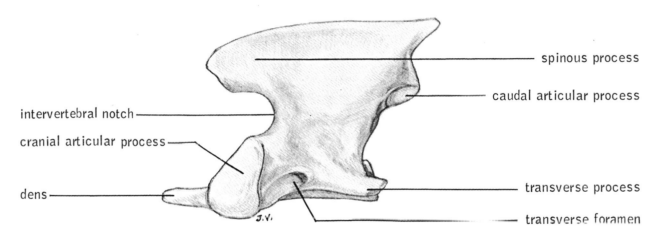

intervertebral notch

cranial articular process

dens

spinous process

caudal articular process

transverse process

transverse foramen

Typical Cervical Vertebra - Caudal View

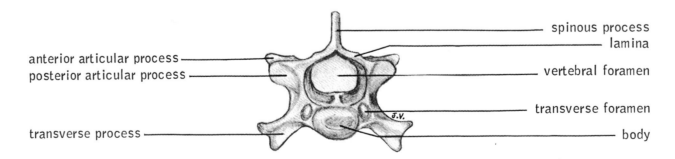

anterior articular process
posterior articular process

transverse process

spinous process
lamina

vertebral foramen

transverse foramen

body

Figure 6: Cervical Vertebrae

Thoracic Vertebra - Lateral View

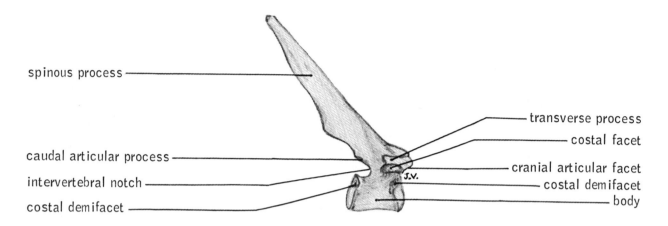

spinous process ———————————————————

transverse process
costal facet

caudal articular process ————————————
intervertebral notch ————————————————
costal demifacet ————————————————————

cranial articular facet
costal demifacet
body

Thoracic Vertebra - Cranial View

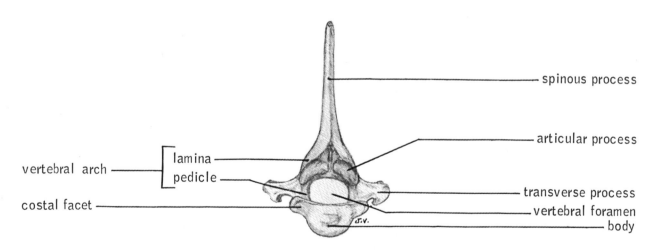

spinous process

articular process

vertebral arch ———
costal facet ————————

lamina
pedicle

transverse process
vertebral foramen
body

Figure 7: Thoracic Vertebrae

Typical Lumbar Vertebra - Anterior View

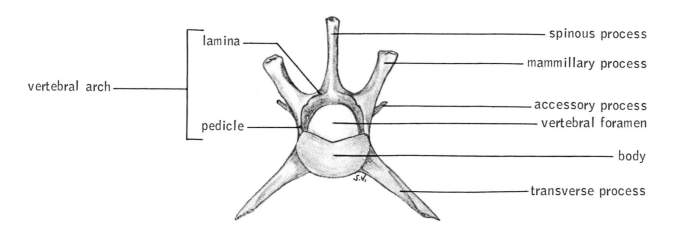

vertebral arch

lamina

pedicle

spinous process

mammillary process

accessory process

vertebral foramen

body

transverse process

Typical Lumbar Vertebra - Lateral View

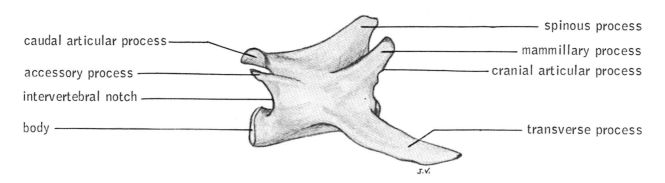

caudal articular process

accessory process

intervertebral notch

body

spinous process

mammillary process

cranial articular process

transverse process

Sacrum - Dorsal View

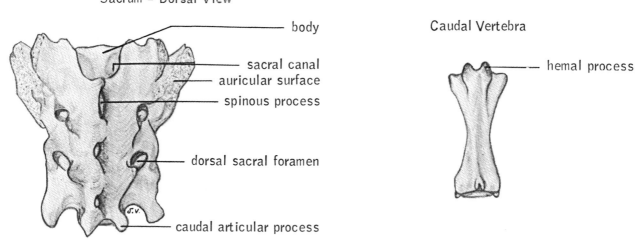

body

sacral canal

auricular surface

spinous process

dorsal sacral foramen

caudal articular process

Caudal Vertebra

hemal process

Figure 8: Sacrum, Lumbar and Caudal Vertebrae

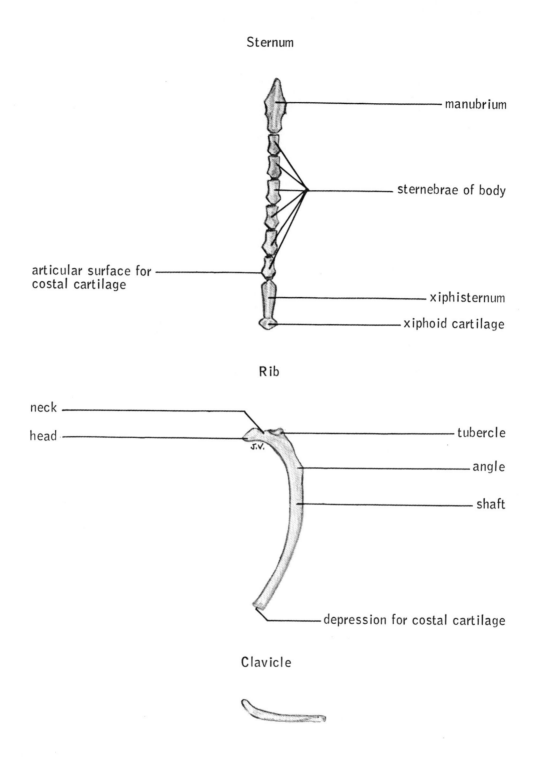

Sternum

manubrium

sternebrae of body

articular surface for costal cartilage

xiphisternum

xiphoid cartilage

Rib

neck

head

J.V.

tubercle

angle

shaft

depression for costal cartilage

Clavicle

Figure 9: Sternum, Rib, and Clavicle

Scapula - Left Medial View

Scapula - Left Lateral View

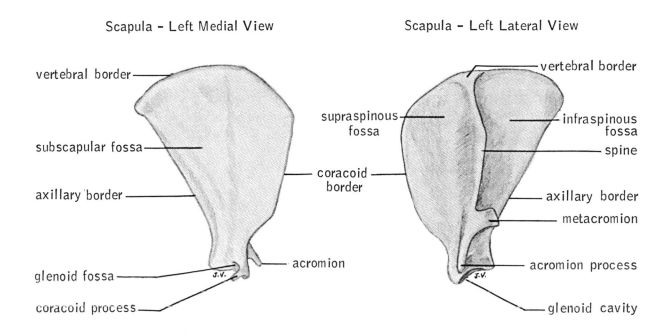

vertebral border

subscapular fossa

axillary border

glenoid fossa

coracoid process

supraspinous fossa

coracoid border

acromion

vertebral border

infraspinous fossa

spine

axillary border

metacromion

acromion process

glenoid cavity

Lateral View of Os Coxae

Medial View of Os Coxae

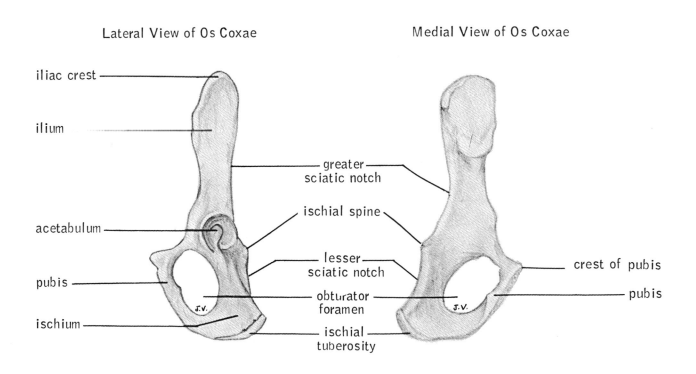

iliac crest

ilium

acetabulum

pubis

ischium

greater sciatic notch

ischial spine

lesser sciatic notch

obturator foramen

ischial tuberosity

crest of pubis

pubis

Figure 10: Scapula and Os Coxae (Innominate)

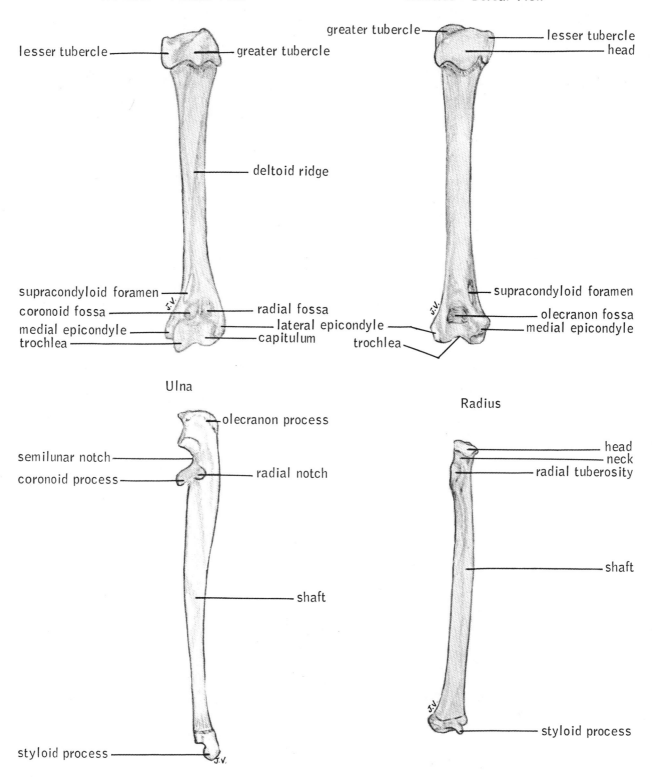

Humerus – Ventral View

lesser tubercle ——
—— greater tubercle

—— deltoid ridge

supracondyloid foramen ——
coronoid fossa ——
medial epicondyle ——
trochlea ——
—— radial fossa
—— lateral epicondyle
—— capitulum

Humerus – Dorsal View

greater tubercle ——
—— lesser tubercle
—— head

—— supracondyloid foramen
—— olecranon fossa
—— medial epicondyle
trochlea ——

Ulna

—— olecranon process

semilunar notch ——
coronoid process ——
—— radial notch

—— shaft

styloid process ——

Radius

—— head
—— neck
—— radial tuberosity

—— shaft

—— styloid process

Figure 11: Bones of the Left Foreleg

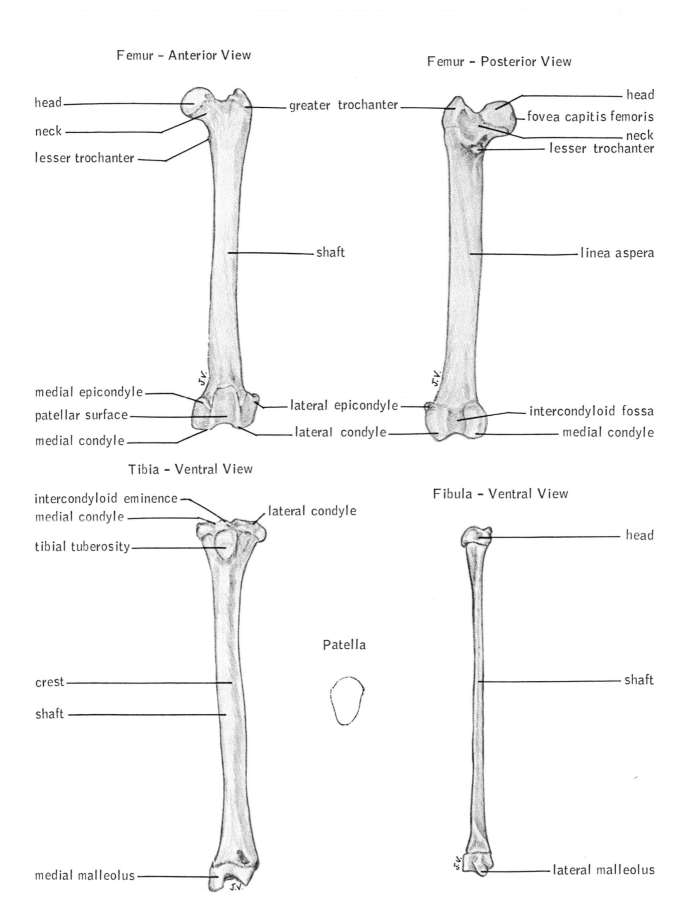

Femur – Anterior View

head
neck
lesser trochanter
greater trochanter
shaft
medial epicondyle
patellar surface
medial condyle
lateral epicondyle
lateral condyle

Femur – Posterior View

head
fovea capitis femoris
neck
lesser trochanter
linea aspera
intercondyloid fossa
medial condyle

Tibia – Ventral View

intercondyloid eminence
medial condyle
tibial tuberosity
lateral condyle
crest
shaft
medial malleolus

Patella

Fibula – Ventral View

head
shaft
lateral malleolus

Figure 12: Bones of Left Hindlimb

Skinning the Cat

PROCEDURE

1. Lay the cat on its ventral surface. Lift up the skin on the dorsal neck region and make a small longitudinal slit in the midline through the skin. Be very careful not to cut completely through the superficial fascia beneath the skin. The skin is about 1/4th inch thick.

2. Continue the incision down the center of the back to the base of the tail (see Figure 13). There is a sheet of deep fascia in the midline of the back that is part of the trapezius muscle. Be especially careful not to cut through this sheet of deep fascia.

3. Make additional incisions through the skin around the neck, down the lateral surface of each leg, and around the wrist and ankles (as illustrated in Figure 13). The skin should be left on the head, tail, feet, and perineum (the area between the pubic symphysis and the coccyx).

4. Beginning on the back, gradually separate the skin from the underlying muscles. This can be done easily by pulling the skin back towards you with one hand, and separating the skin from the fascia by gently pressing the fingers of the other hand or a scalpel against the skin.

5. Note the fine, parallel, brownish muscle fibers that adhere to the undersurface of the skin. This is one of the dermal muscles, the cutaneous maximus. This muscle originates from the latissimus dorsi, the pectoralis group of muscles, and from the linea alba, and inserts on much of the skin. Behind the armpits it adheres to the latissimus dorsi and to the pectoralis group, and it should be left on the body of the cat. The cutaneous maximus moves the skin of the cat and is not found in man.

6. The platysma, another dermal muscle, is in the neck region of both man and the cat. It is generally removed with the skin.

7. The cutaneous blood vessels and nerves must be cut. These can be seen passing out to the skin. The mammary glands should also be removed with the skin. In the female cat these appear as large glandular masses along the ventral surface of the thorax and abdomen.

8. Continue skinning the back around to the lateral surface of the cat; then remove the skin from the legs being careful not to damage the great saphenous vein on the thigh and leg.

9. Beginning at the ventral surface of the neck (avoid damage to the external jugular vein), remove the skin down to the wad of fat in the groin.

10. If directions have been followed, the skin may now be removed in one piece. Either the skin or moist paper towels may be used to wrap the cat between laboratory periods to prevent drying.

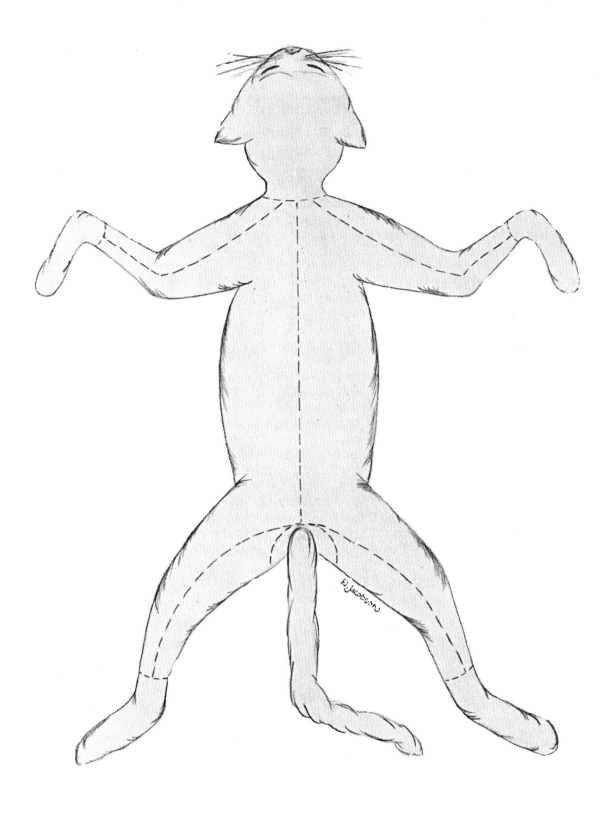

Figure 13: Skinning the Cat

The Musculature of the Cat

As you dissect the muscles of the cat, determine the major differences between them and those in man. As you locate the origin of the muscle (the site of attachment to a fixed bone) and the insertion (the attachment to a more freely movable bone), determine the function of the muscle. Remember that as a muscle contracts, it pulls the insertion towards the origin. Muscles are usually attached to bones by tendons, which are bands of dense white fibrous connective tissue. Some muscles insert by means of an aponeurosis, a broad flattened tendon.

In each of the following exercises, attempt to locate each muscle before making any incisions. It will be necessary to clean the surface of each of the muscles, by gently pulling off or cutting away superficial fascia and fat, in order to see the direction of the muscle fibers. Usually all the fibers of a muscle will run in one direction, while the fibers of an adjacent muscle will run in a different direction.

Do not cut into the fibers of the muscles you are separating. The groups of fibers comprising a muscle are surrounded by deep fascia. This fascia should not be removed from the muscle. If the muscle fibers are visible, it means that the muscle has been cut into, rather than being separated from adjacent muscles.

In order to examine the deep muscles, it is frequently necessary to sever a superficial muscle. Do not bisect a muscle unless directed to do so. To bisect means to cut into two parts. When bisecting a muscle, make an incision through it, at right angles to the direction of the muscle fibers, and halfway between the origin and the insertion. In order to see the underlying muscles, it is then necessary to reflect the superficial muscle (pull the ends back - one towards the origin and the other towards the insertion). If these directions are followed, the origin and insertion of the muscle will be retained.

Part 1. The Superficial Muscles of the Chest

PROCEDURE

1. Clean the surface of the muscles on the left side of the chest. It is not necessary to dissect the right side unless errors have been made on the left.

2. The pectoralis muscles are the large muscles covering the ventral chest. The group arises from the sternum and inserts, for the most part, on the humerus. There are four subdivisions of the pectoralis muscle in the cat, but only two in man. Locate the four subdivisions of the muscle by comparing the specimen with Figure 14.

3. The pectoantebrachialis is a band of parallel fibers, about one-half inch wide, that extends from the manubrium of the sternum to insert on the fascia of the forearm. The anterior edge of this muscle is about one-third of an inch from the beginning of the entire pectoralis group; it passes across the rest of the pectoralis. Separate this muscle from the underlying fascia and muscle, then bisect and reflect.

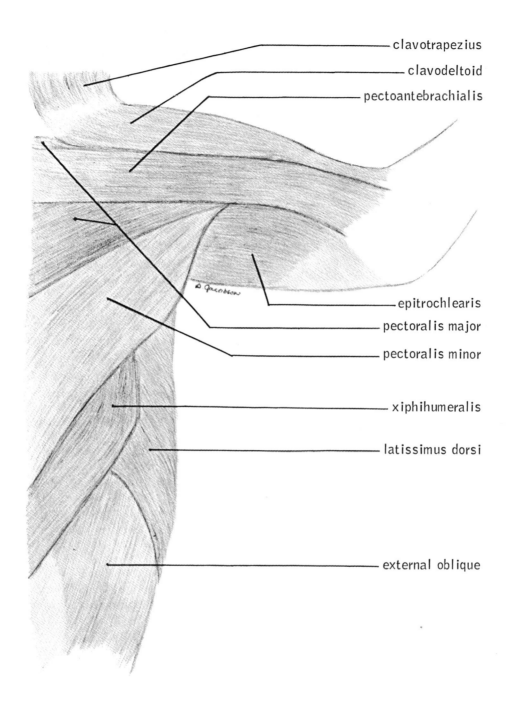

clavotrapezius

clavodeltoid

pectoantebrachialis

epitrochlearis

pectoralis major

pectoralis minor

xiphihumeralis

latissimus dorsi

external oblique

Figure 14: Ventral View of Chest Musculature

4. The muscle on the shoulder anterior to the pectoantebrachialis is the clavodeltoid (clavobrachialis). This muscle is part of the deltoid group. Lift up the clavodeltoid and separate it from the connective tissue underneath. You can feel the clavicle on the underside of the medial end of this muscle. The clavodeltoid arises on the clavicle and clavotrapezius and inserts on the ulna with the pectoantebrachialis. It may be considered as a continuation of the clavotrapezius onto the shoulder. Do not bisect this muscle.

5. The pectoralis major is the portion of the pectoralis group deep to the pectoantebrachialis and the clavodeltoid. It originates on the upper part of the sternum, and inserts along much of the humerus. It is folded on itself and may appear double. Do not try to separate this muscle into two muscles. The fibers of the pectoralis major parallel those of the pectoantebrachialis.

6. The posterior border of the pectoralis major may be located by noting that the pectoralis minor approaches the major at an angle and then passes underneath it. Loosen the anterior and posterior borders of the pectoralis major. Separate the muscle from the underlying pectoralis minor. Bisect and reflect the muscle. Note its wide insertion on the humerus.

7. The pectoralis minor lies posterior (and dorsal in part) to the pectoralis major. It originates on the middle portion of the sternum and inserts near the proximal end of the humerus. This muscle is larger than the major in the cat. It is not equivalent to the pectoralis minor in the human. Bisect and reflect the muscle, being careful not to sever underlying veins and arteries.

8. The xiphihumeralis, the fourth subdivision of the pectoralis group, arises from the xiphoid process of the sternum, posterior to the pectoralis minor. The fibers run parallel to the pectoralis minor and eventually pass deep to this muscle to insert on the humerus. The fibers of the xiphihumeralis fuse on the posterior edge with a portion of the latissimus dorsi. Bisect the xiphihumeralis.

Part 2. The Superficial Muscles of the Neck and Shoulder

PROCEDURE

1. Remove additional skin up to the ear from the left side of the neck. Do not injure the external jugular vein, the large vein which lies on the ventral surface of the neck. Free this vein from the underlying muscles. (Refer to Figure 15 during this dissection.)

2. Clean off the connective tissue from the back of the left shoulder, and from the ventral and lateral surfaces of the left neck. Do not remove the fascia in the midline of the back, since this is part of the origin of the trapezius muscle.

3. Examine the ventral surface of the neck. Locate the sternomastoid, (see Figure 15), the band of muscle that extends from the manubrium of the sternum diagonally towards the mastoid region of the skull. The muscle passes deep to the external jugular vein. The sternomastoid turns and bends the head. Free both borders of this muscle. Do not bisect.

4. The sternohyoids, a narrow pair of muscles which may be fused in the midline, lie along the mid-ventral line of the neck. The posterior ends are

20

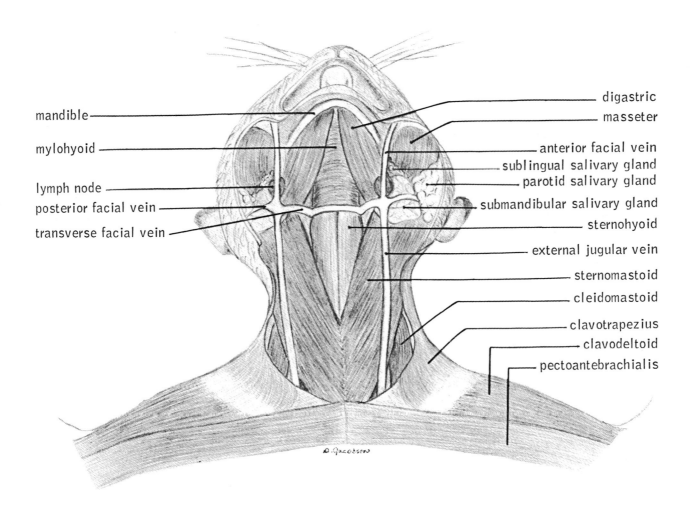

mandible

mylohyoid

lymph node

posterior facial vein

transverse facial vein

digastric

masseter

anterior facial vein

sublingual salivary gland

parotid salivary gland

submandibular salivary gland

sternohyoid

external jugular vein

sternomastoid

cleidomastoid

clavotrapezius

clavodeltoid

pectoantebrachialis

Figure 15: Ventral View of Neck Musculature

covered by the sternomastoid. The sternohyoids extend from the first costal cartilage and the sternum to the hyoid bone which they depress.

5. In order to locate the next muscle, the cleidomastoid, again locate the sternomastoid. The cleidomastoid is a narrow deep band of muscle found between the clavotrapezius and the sternomastoid. It originates on the clavicle deep to the clavotrapezius and inserts on the mastoid region of the temporal bone. The anterior portion of the cleidomastoid passes deep to the sternomastoid. Much of the cleidomastoid is under the clavotrapezius (see step No. 9). Free the cleidomastoid along both borders. Do not bisect. In man the lower ends of the sternomastoid and cleidomastoid muscles are separate, but they are fused near the mastoid; therefore this compound muscle is known as the sternocleidomastoid.

6. The digastric muscle is the superficial muscle extending along the inner surface of the mandible (see Figure 15). It runs from the occipital and temporal bones to the mandible and depresses the lower jaw.

7. The superficial muscle running transversely in the midline and passing deep to the digastric is the mylohyoid. It is a thin, sheetlike muscle, originating on the mandible and inserting on the median raphe. It raises the floor of the mouth (Figure 15).

8. Locate the large parotid salivary gland anterior to the ear (Figure 15). The large muscle mass anterior and ventral to the parotid at the angle of each jaw is the masseter muscle. It extends from the zygomatic arch to the mandible and elevates the mandible.

9. The trapezius group of muscles covers much of the dorsal surface of the scapula (see Figure 16). The clavotrapezius is the broad muscle located on the back and side of the neck dorsal to the cleidomastoid. It originates from the occipital bone and the first few cervical vertebrae and inserts on the clavicle. It elevates the clavicle. The clavodeltoid continues from the clavicle, the insertion of the clavotrapezius, to the ulna. Therefore the clavotrapezius can be located by determining the origin of the clavodeltoid. The clavotrapezius is the muscle dorsal and anterior to the clavodeltoid. Free these two muscles from the underlying fascia. Do not bisect.

10. The acromiotrapezius (see Figure 16) covers the upper part of the scapula. It arises from fascia along the mid-dorsal line and inserts on the spine and acromion process of the scapula.

11. The triangular sheet of muscle on the back, posterior to the acromiotrapezius, is the spinotrapezius (Figure 16). It arises from the thoracic vertebrae and inserts on the scapula. Separate this muscle from underlying muscles. Free the anterior and posterior borders of both the acromiotrapezius and spinotrapezius muscles. Do not bisect these at this time. These muscles adduct the scapula. In man these three separate muscles are merged into one large trapezius muscle which adducts and elevates the scapula and extends and rotates the head.

12. The latissimus dorsi, the large muscle posterior to the trapezius group, arises from the spines of the thoracic vertebrae and the lumbodorsal fascia (Figure 16). It runs anteriorly and ventrally to insert on the proximal end of the humerus with the xiphihumeralis. It extends the humerus. Free the anterior and posterior edges of the latissimus dorsi. (Part of the anterior border lies beneath the spinotrapezius.)

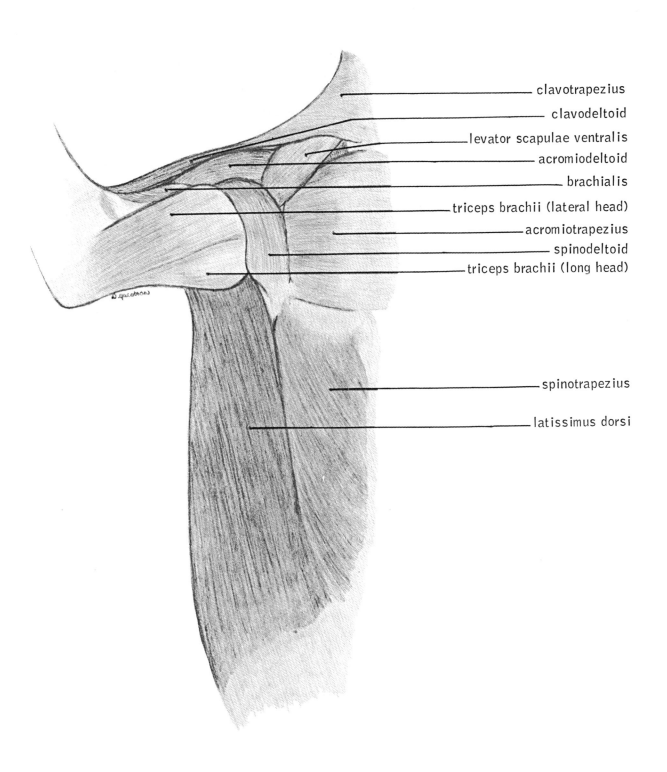

clavotrapezius

clavodeltoid

levator scapulae ventralis

acromiodeltoid

brachialis

triceps brachii (lateral head)

acromiotrapezius

spinodeltoid

triceps brachii (long head)

spinotrapezius

latissimus dorsi

Figure 16: Superficial Muscles of the Back

23

13. The straplike band of muscle in the cat that lies on the side of the neck between the clavotrapezius and the acromiotrapezius is the levator scapulae ventralis. It arises from the atlas and the occipital and passes posteriorly beneath the clavotrapezius to insert on the acromion process of the scapula. It pulls the scapula forward. (See Figure 16.) This muscle is not found in man.

14. The deltoid muscle, which flexes, extends, rotates, and abducts the humerus, lies lateral to and below the insertion of the levator scapulae ventralis (Figure 16). It is subdivided into three parts in the cat. The clavodeltoid (clavo-brachialis) seen earlier, originates on the clavicle and inserts on the ulna, flexing the forearm. This is the most anterior portion of the muscle.

15. The spinodeltoid, the most posterior portion, originates on the scapula ventral to the insertion of the acromiotrapezius. It runs almost parallel with the edge of the spine of the scapula. It inserts on the proximal humerus. Free the borders of the muscle.

16. Locate the acromiodeltoid, the middle muscle of this group, posterior to the clavodeltoid. It originates from the acromion process of the scapula deep to the levator scapulae ventralis and inserts on the proximal end of the humerus. It is not necessary to dissect out this muscle, which may appear double at its origin.

Part 3. The Deeper Muscles of the Back and Shoulder

PROCEDURE

1. In order to expose the deeper muscles of the shoulder and back, carefully bisect the acromiotrapezius and spinotrapezius muscles through muscle fibers halfway between their origins and insertions. Reflect the muscle fibers. Next bisect and reflect the latissimus dorsi.

2. The supraspinatus muscle fills the supraspinous fossa of the scapula; the infraspinatus muscle fills the infraspinous fossa. Both muscles (see Figure 17) originate on the scapula and insert on the humerus. The supraspinatus extends the humerus and the infraspinatus rotates it laterally.

3. The teres major muscle (see Figure 17) originates on the axillary border of the scapula posterior to the infraspinatus. It inserts on the proximal end of the humerus with the latissimus dorsi. Separate the teres major from the infraspinatus. Do not bisect this muscle, which extends and rotates the humerus.

4. Pull the scapula away from the vertebral column. The large muscle that arises from the posterior cervical and anterior thoracic vertebrae and inserts along the vertebral border of the scapula is the rhomboideus minor. The rhomboideus major is immediately posterior to this, inserting on the dorsal posterior angle of the scapula. Some authors refer to these two muscles as one, the rhomboideus. In man, the rhomboideus major is larger than the minor. These two muscles draw the scapula dorsally and rotate it.

5. The rhomboideus capitis is the most anterior muscle of this group. It is a narrow, thin, ribbonlike muscle, which draws the scapula forward, extending from the occipital bone to the scapula on the side of the rhomboideus minor muscle. It elevates and rotates the scapula. In man, this muscle is united with the rhomboideus minor. (See Figure 17.)

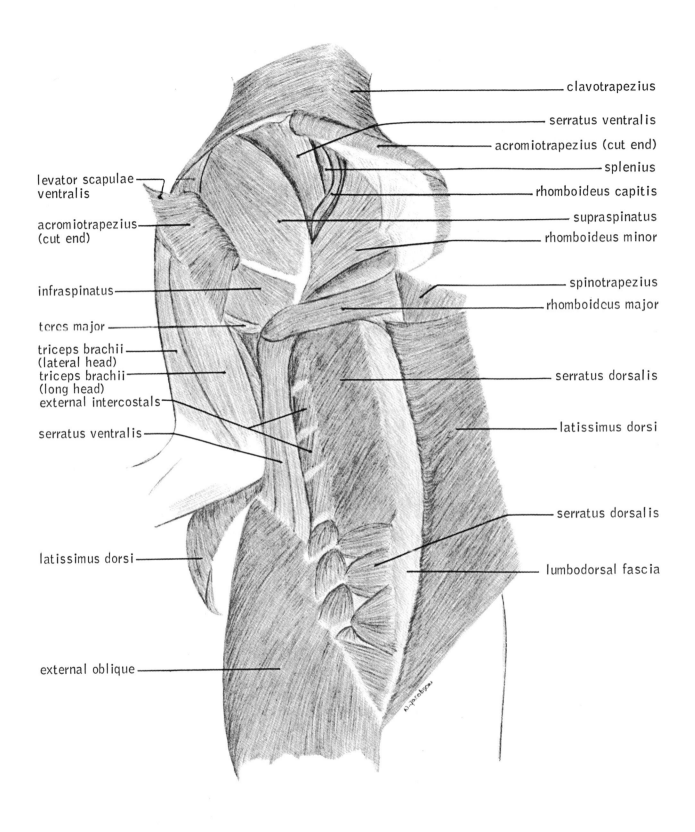

clavotrapezius

serratus ventralis

acromiotrapezius (cut end)

splenius

rhomboideus capitis

supraspinatus

rhomboideus minor

spinotrapezius

rhomboideus major

serratus dorsalis

latissimus dorsi

serratus dorsalis

lumbodorsal fascia

levator scapulae ventralis

acromiotrapezius (cut end)

infraspinatus

teres major

triceps brachii (lateral head)

triceps brachii (long head)

external intercostals

serratus ventralis

latissimus dorsi

external oblique

Figure 17: Deep Muscles of the Shoulder

6. Deep to this muscle is a broad flat muscle, the splenius. It covers most of the dorsal and lateral surface of the neck; its action is to turn the head.

7. Pull the scapula laterally. The large fan-shaped muscle originating by separate slips from the ribs, passing ventral to the scapula, and inserting on the vertebral border of the scapula is the serratus ventralis (see Figure 18). This muscle is also visible on the lateral surface of the body at its origin. Do not bisect. This muscle pulls the scapula forward and down.

8. The subscapular fossa of the scapula is filled with the subscapularis muscle (see Figure 19) which inserts on the humerus and rotates it medially. Do not dissect or bisect.

Part 4. The Muscles of the Brachium and Antebrachium

PROCEDURE

1. Clear away the fascia from the brachium.

2. Locate the epitrochlearis, a flat muscle that arises from the surface of the latissimus dorsi, extends along the medial surface of the arm, and inserts on the olecranon process of the ulna. This muscle is not present in man. Bisect this muscle and reflect. The long head of the triceps brachii lies posterior to this muscle. (See Figure 19.)

3. Now examine the posterior surface of the arm. The triceps brachii is the large muscle with three main heads; these cover the posterior surface and much of the sides of the humerus. It extends the forearm. Separate the subdivisions of the triceps. Refer to Figures 17 and 18. The long head, located on the posterior surface of the humerus, is the largest. Note that it arises from the scapula posterior to the glenoid cavity and inserts on the olecranon process. Free both borders of the long head.

4. Locate the lateral head, the large head that originates from the proximal end of the humerus and covers much of the lateral surface of the humerus. Bisect and reflect the lateral head.

5. A long narrow medial head can be found beneath the lateral head. This is slightly below the visible portion of the humerus.

6. The triceps of the cat has a fourth head, the anconeus, a tiny muscle which lies deep to the distal end of the lateral head of the triceps. (See Figure 18.)

7. The brachialis (Figure 18) can be seen on the ventrolateral surface of the humerus, anterior to the lateral head of the triceps. It arises from the humerus and inserts on the proximal end of the ulna. The brachialis flexes the forearm.

8. The biceps brachii lies on the ventromedial surface of the humerus. It originates on the scapula and inserts on the radius. Much of this muscle lies beneath the insertion of the pectoralis major and minor. (Reflect the pectoralis group to the humerus if this was not done previously.) Trace the biceps to its insertion. This muscle flexes the forearm. (See Figure 19.)

9. Next locate the tiny coracobrachialis muscle beneath the pectoralis. This is a small muscle extending from the coracoid process of the scapula to the proximal end of the humerus. It adducts the arm.

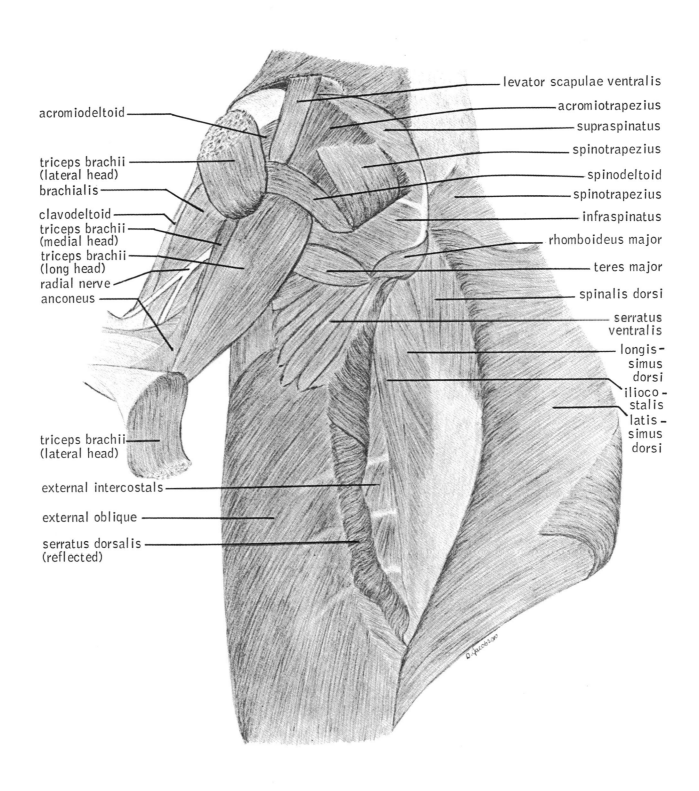

acromiodeltoid

triceps brachii
(lateral head)
brachialis

clavodeltoid
triceps brachii
(medial head)
triceps brachii
(long head)
radial nerve
anconeus

triceps brachii
(lateral head)

external intercostals

external oblique

serratus dorsalis
(reflected)

levator scapulae ventralis
acromiotrapezius
supraspinatus
spinotrapezius
spinodeltoid
spinotrapezius
infraspinatus
rhomboideus major
teres major
spinalis dorsi
serratus
ventralis
longis-
simus
dorsi
ilioco-
stalis
latis-
simus
dorsi

Figure 18: Deep Muscles of the Shoulder,
Back, and Arm

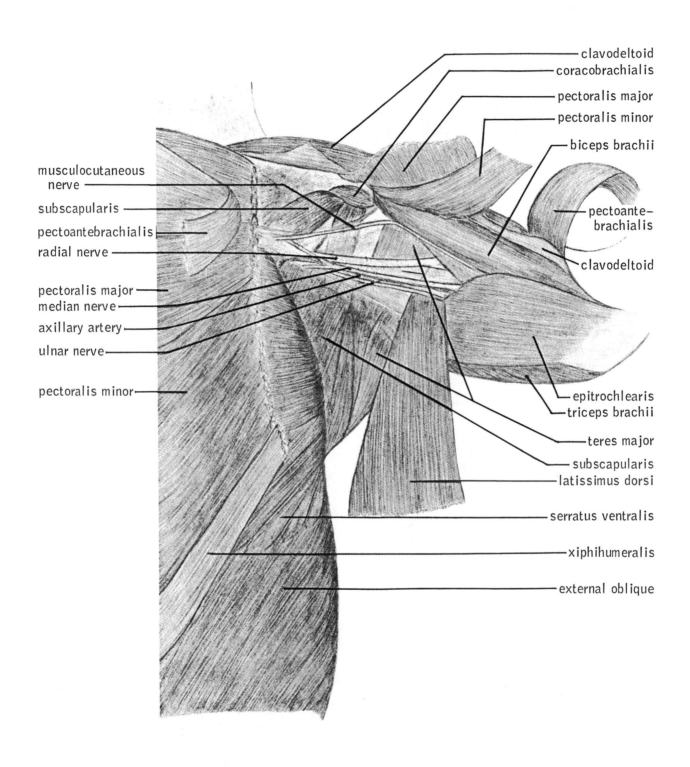

clavodeltoid
coracobrachialis
pectoralis major
pectoralis minor
biceps brachii

musculocutaneous
nerve

subscapularis

pectoantebrachialis

radial nerve

pectoantebrachialis

clavodeltoid

pectoralis major
median nerve
axillary artery
ulnar nerve

pectoralis minor

epitrochlearis
triceps brachii

teres major

subscapularis
latissimus dorsi

serratus ventralis

xiphihumeralis

external oblique

Figure 19: Deep View of Muscles of the Chest and Brachium

10. Optional: locate the <u>teres</u> <u>minor</u> muscle, a small muscle between the infraspinatus and the triceps. Reflect the lateral head of the triceps and push the spinodeltoid dorsally. Look deep between the proximal end of the triceps and the infraspinatus. The teres minor appears to be the lateral edge of the infraspinatus. This muscle rotates the humerus.

11. Optional: note the tough layer of deep fascia which covers the forearm muscles. Observe the tendons of these muscles at the wrist. Separate the superficial muscles of the forearm. Do not bisect any of these muscles. Compare your dissection with Figures 20 and 21. Identify each of the labeled muscles. The dorsal group of muscles, in general, extend and supinate. The ventral group of muscles are flexors and pronators.

12. Separate the <u>extensor digitorum</u> lateralis from the <u>extensor indicus proprius</u> muscle (see Figure 22). The <u>extensor pollicis brevis</u> and <u>supinator</u> are now visible.

Part 5. The Abdominal Wall Muscles

PROCEDURE

1. Clean off the ventral and lateral surfaces of the left side of the trunk between the xiphihumeralis and the pelvic regions. Note the <u>lumbodorsal fascia</u>, the wide sheet of white fascia covering the lumbar region of the back.

2. As in man, the lateral abdominal wall of the cat is composed of three layers of muscle. These abdominal muscles are very thin; therefore, be very careful to cut through only one layer at a time.

3. The lateral abdominal wall muscles serve to compress the abdomen. This action is important in forced expiration, defecation, micturition, and parturition. They are also important in flexion and lateral flexion of the trunk.

4. The <u>external oblique</u> forms the outermost layer of the lateral abdominal muscles. Note that part of its origin lies beneath the posterior edge of the latissimus dorsi muscle. It originates on the posterior ribs and the lumbodorsal fascia. (See Figure 23 for this step and for steps 5-12.)

5. Make a <u>shallow</u> longitudinal incision (about five inches long) through the external oblique along the lateral surface of the abdomen. Extend this incision from the ribs to the pelvis. Do not cut deeply; as you cut, watch for a deeper layer of muscle having a different fiber direction. When the deeper layer is reached, reflect the external oblique towards the midline and towards its origin.

6. Note the <u>aponeurosis</u> of the external oblique. Lift the muscle up and notice that the muscle fibers terminate at least an inch before the <u>linea alba</u>, the mid-ventral line formed by the union of the aponeuroses of the lateral abdominal wall muscles. The aponeurosis is ventral to the rectus abdominis muscle.

7. Observe the posterior border of the external oblique. In man this thickened border is called the inguinal ligament. This is not apparent in the cat.

8. The <u>internal oblique</u> lies beneath the external oblique, with the fibers running in the <u>opposite direction</u> (ventral and anterior). It originates on the lumbodorsal fascia and inserts on the linea alba.

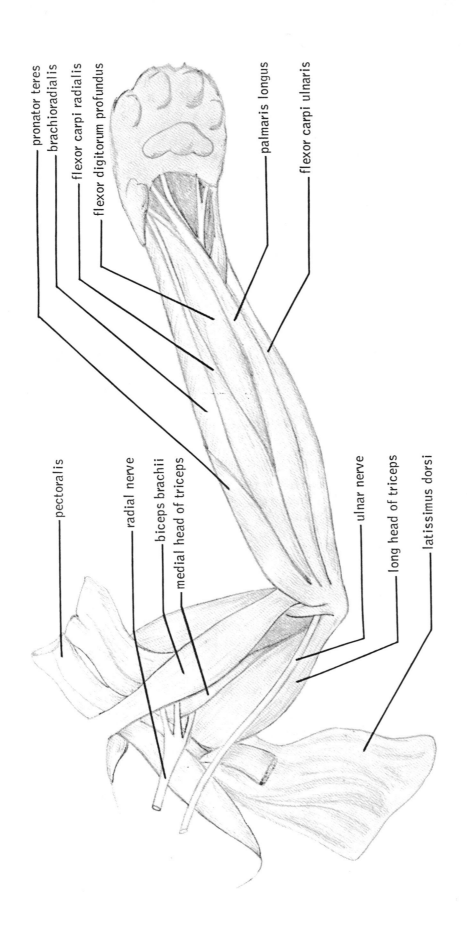

pronator teres
brachioradialis
flexor carpi radialis
flexor digitorum profundus

palmaris longus
flexor carpi ulnaris

pectoralis
radial nerve
biceps brachii
medial head of triceps

ulnar nerve
long head of triceps
latissimus dorsi

Figure 20: Ventral View of the Superficial Muscles of the Forearm

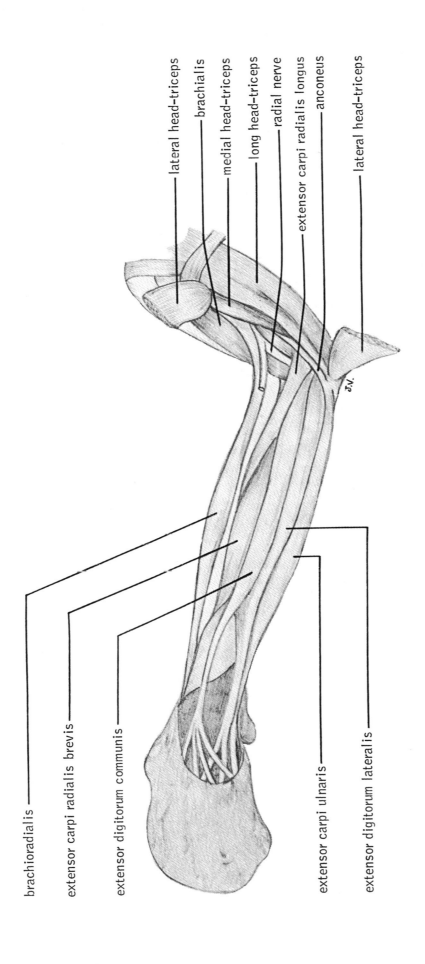

lateral head–triceps

brachialis

medial head–triceps

long head–triceps

radial nerve

extensor carpi radialis longus

anconeus

lateral head–triceps

brachioradialis

extensor carpi radialis brevis

extensor digitorum communis

extensor carpi ulnaris

extensor digitorum lateralis

Figure 21: Dorsal View of Muscles of Forearm

31

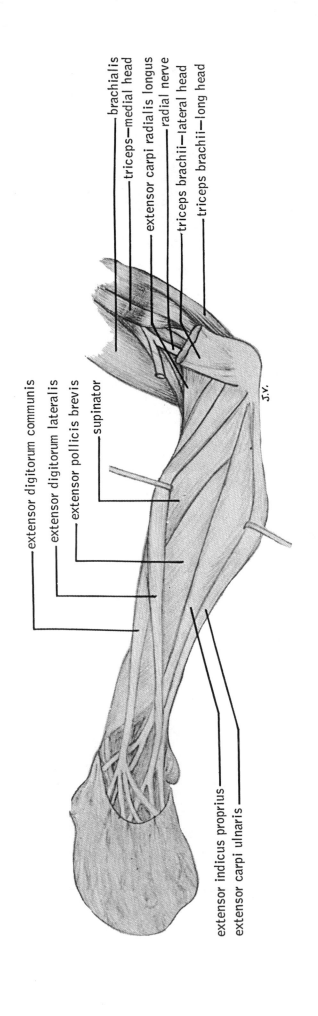

brachialis

triceps—medial head

extensor carpi radialis longus

radial nerve

triceps brachii—lateral head

triceps brachii—long head

extensor digitorum communis

extensor digitorum lateralis

extensor pollicis brevis

supinator

j.v.

extensor indicus proprius

extensor carpi ulnaris

Figure 22: Deep View of Muscles of Dorsal Forearm

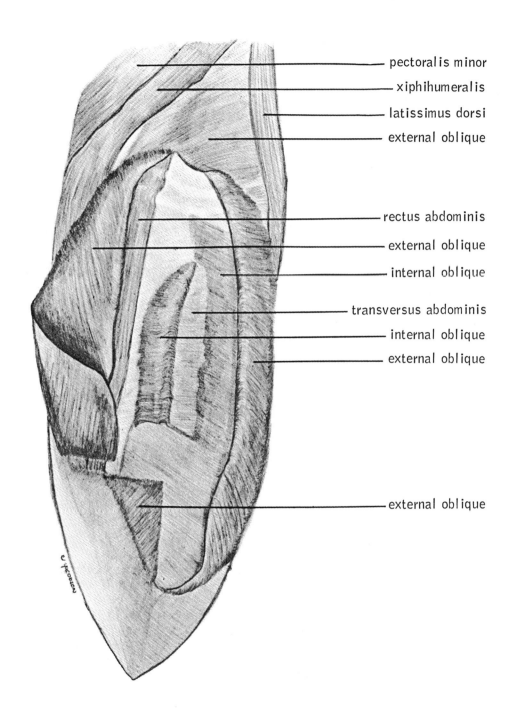

pectoralis minor

xiphihumeralis

latissimus dorsi

external oblique

rectus abdominis

external oblique

internal oblique

transversus abdominis

internal oblique

external oblique

external oblique

Figure 23: Abdominal Wall Musculature (lateral view)

9. Make a four inch longitudinal incision through the muscle fibers of the internal oblique on the lateral side of the abdominal cavity. Watch closely for the transverse muscle fibers of the transversus abdominis, the muscle extending from the vertebral column, the lumbodorsal fascia, and the sacrum to the linea alba. Reflect the internal oblique towards the midline until its aponeurosis becomes visible.

10. Carefully separate some of the fibers of the transversus abdominis. The shiny membrane visible beneath the muscle fibers is the parietal layer of the peritoneum, which should not be pierced.

11. In order to locate the rectus abdominis, the longitudinal band of muscle lying lateral to the linea alba, reflect the external oblique. The rectus abdominis, extending from the pubis to the sternum and costal cartilage, supports the abdominal wall, especially during pregnancy. Do not dissect out this muscle.

12. In mammals such as the pig, fat is deposited in the connective tissue layers between the muscles of the lateral abdominal wall so that the fat and muscle alternate. This part of the pig is sold commercially as bacon. The small pieces of cartilage often found in bacon are pieces of costal cartilage from the lower ends of the ribs.

Part 6. Superficial Muscles of the Thigh and Buttocks

PROCEDURE

1. Remove the fat and fascia from the surface of the thigh and buttocks region. Be especially careful not to damage any muscles in the gluteal region as the fascia adheres tightly to the gluteal muscles. Start to separate the more obvious muscles. Do not remove any blood vessels from the thigh.

2. Observe the two large superficial muscles on the ventromedial surface of the thigh (see Figure 24). The sartorius is the more lateral of the two. It is about 1 1/2 inches wide and resembles a flattened band. Loosen the lateral edges from the ilium to the tibia and bisect. The sartorius adducts and rotates the thigh.

3. The gracilis (Figure 24) is the large wide, flat muscle covering the medial surface of the ventral thigh below the sartorius. Free both borders of this muscle. Bisect and reflect it, being careful not to completely reflect the insertion of the muscle (see Figure 27). The gracilis originates on the os coxae bone and inserts on the tibia and fascia of the shank. It adducts the thigh.

4. There are four small muscles visible between the sartorius and the gracilis on the ventral surface of the thigh. Immediately above the gracilis a small portion of the adductor femoris muscle is visible. The largest part of this muscle is beneath the gracilis and will be described with the deep muscles of the thigh. (See Figures 24 and 27.)

5. Immediately anterior to the adductor femoris muscle is the narrow adductor longus muscle, also to be described with the adductor muscles. Anterior to the adductor longus muscle is the pectineus. This muscle is a deep, small muscle posterior to the femoral artery and vein. The pectineus originates on the pubis and inserts on the femur; it extends the thigh. Above the pectineus is the iliopsoas muscle, a compound muscle originating from the

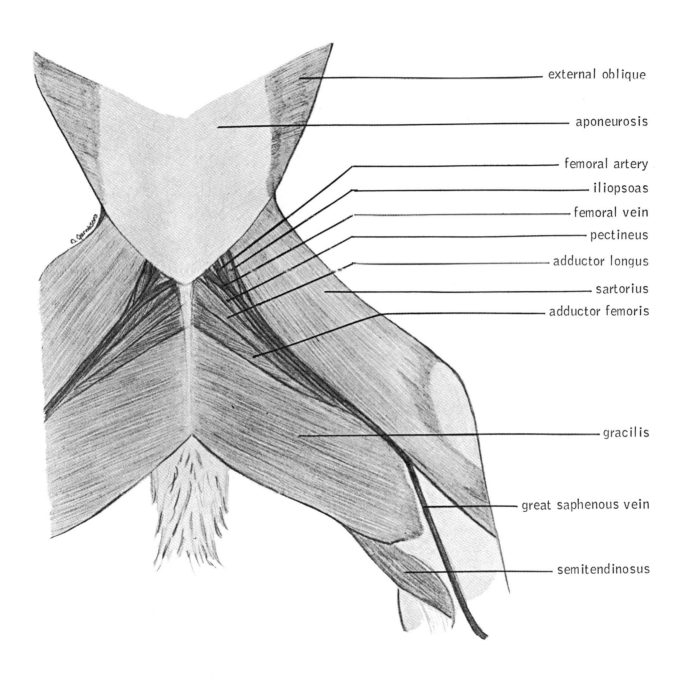

external oblique

aponeurosis

femoral artery

iliopsoas

femoral vein

pectineus

adductor longus

sartorius

adductor femoris

gracilis

great saphenous vein

semitendinosus

Figure 24: Ventral View of Superficial Thigh Muscles

35

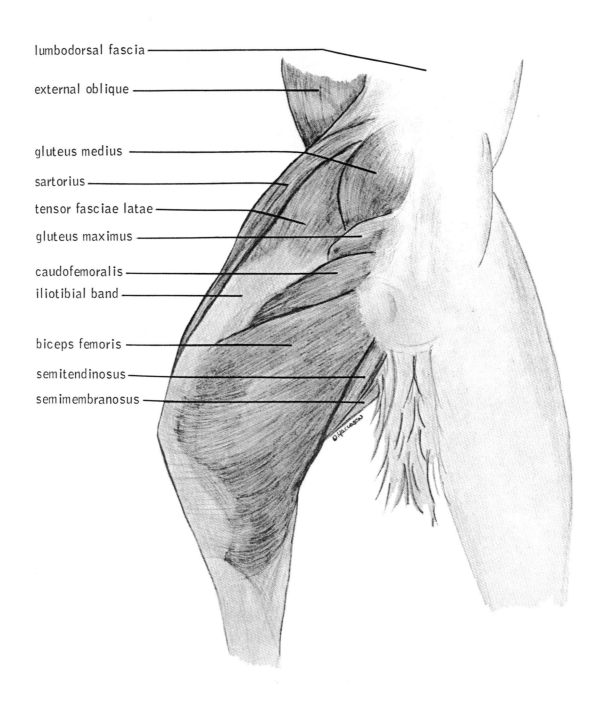

lumbodorsal fascia

external oblique

gluteus medius

sartorius

tensor fasciae latae

gluteus maximus

caudofemoralis

iliotibial band

biceps femoris

semitendinosus

semimembranosus

Figure 25: Superficial Muscles of the Thigh and Buttocks, dorsal view

lumbar vertebrae and ilium and inserting on the femur; it rotates and flexes the thigh. Only a small portion of the iliopsoas is visible. It may be seen anterior to the femoral artery and veins. Its fibers run nearly at right angles to the blood vessels. (Figure 24.)

6. Dorsal to the sartorius on the lateral surface of the thigh can be seen a tough white band of fascia. This is the lateral thickening of the fascia lata, the iliotibial band. In order to free the lateral boundary of the iliotibial band, lift the lateral border of the sartorius. Pass your fingers beneath the tough fascia of the iliotibial band dorsally. With the scalpel, separate the medial border of the iliotibial band from the biceps femoris. When the iliotibial band is raised up, a triangular muscle mass, the tensor fasciae latae, can be seen inserting on the proximal end of the iliotibial band. This muscle is a short wide muscle originating on the ilium and inserting on the fascia lata. It tenses the fascia lata and extends the shank. Locate the boundary between the tensor fasciae latae and the gluteus medius. (See Figure 25.)

7. The broad muscle dorsal to the iliotibial band covering the entire lateral surface of the thigh is the biceps femoris. This muscle forms the lateral wall of the popliteal fossa. It originates on the ischium and inserts on the tibia and fascia of the shank. It abducts the thigh and flexes the shank. Remove the large wad of fat in the popliteal fossa. Free both borders of this muscle. When freeing the lateral border of this muscle, begin with care near the knee and work upward looking for a small muscle, the caudofemoralis, at the anterior end of the muscle. (See Figure 25.)

8. The caudofemoralis is a small muscle anterior to the origin of the biceps femoris, and inferior to the gluteus maximus. It is united with the gluteus maximus in man. It originates on the caudal vertebrae and inserts on the patella by way of a long, very narrow tendon visible on the inner surface of the biceps femoris. (Figure 25.)

9. The gluteus maximus (Figure 25) is immediately anterior to the caudofemoralis. The fibers extend laterally from the sacrum and caudal vertebrae and insert on the proximal femur. It abducts the thigh.

10. The more diagonal fibers anterior to the gluteus maximus form the gluteus medius, which originates on the lateral ilium and the sacral and caudal vertebrae and inserts on the femur (see Figure 25). It abducts the thigh. It is a larger muscle than the gluteus maximus in the cat. Some of the fibers of the gluteus medius pass beneath the gluteus maximus. The two should be carefully separated.

11. The straplike muscle arising from the ischial tuberosity and inserting on the tibia posterior to and medial to the biceps femoris is the semitendinosus. This inch-wide muscle, thicker than the sartorius, forms part of the posteromedial border of the popliteal fossa. It flexes the shank. Free both borders. (Figure 25.)

Part 7. The Deeper Muscles of the Thigh

PROCEDURE

1. Free both borders of the biceps femoris, if this was not done earlier. Be careful not to detach the tendon of the caudofemoralis at the anterior end of the biceps. Gently lift up the biceps, freeing it from the sciatic nerve and

tenuissimus muscle lying beneath. Bisect the biceps and reflect, being careful not to bisect the sciatic nerve. (See Figure 26.)

2. A very thin long muscle can be seen lying beneath the biceps femoris, running parallel to the sciatic nerve. This muscle, the tenuissimus, extends from the second caudal vertebra to the fascia of the biceps femoris. It abducts the thigh and flexes the shank.

3. In order to locate the quadriceps femoris group of muscles, bisect the sartorius, if this was not done earlier. Free both borders of the tensor fasciae latae and the iliotibial band. Bisect the iliotibial band. Reflect this and the tensor fasciae latae. The large muscle now exposed on the anterolateral surface of the thigh is the vastus lateralis. This and the other vasti muscles arise from the upper femur. (See Figures 26 and 27.)

4. Medial to the vastus lateralis on the front of the thigh is a narrow muscle, the rectus femoris, which originates on the ilium (see Figure 27).

5. The muscle on the ventral surface of the thigh medial to the rectus femoris (see Figure 27) is the vastus medialis. Look carefully for the separation between the rectus femoris and the vastus medialis. Bisect the rectus femoris.

6. The deep muscle observed beneath the rectus femoris is the vastus intermedius. These four muscles making up the quadriceps femoris converge and insert on the patella. The patellar ligament then attaches to the tuberosity of the tibia, which is then regarded as the real insertion of the muscle. The entire complex extends the shank.

7. The large muscle medial to the semitendinosus beneath the gracilis is the semimembranosus (see Figure 27). This originates on the ischium, and inserts on the femur. The semimembranosus, the semitendinosus, and the biceps femoris form the hamstring group of muscles.

8. The large muscle anterior to the semimembranosus is the adductor femoris (equivalent to the adductor magnus in man). The tiny adductor longus can be seen anterior to this. The origin of the adductor muscles is the ischium and pubis; they insert on most of the length of the femur and adduct the thigh (see Figure 27). Anterior to the adductor longus muscle is the pectineus muscle. Relocate the iliopsoas muscle (see Part 6, No. 5).

Part 8. Posterior Leg Muscles

PROCEDURE

1. The large calf muscle, the gastrocnemius (see Figure 26) is visible on the posterior leg (shank). Follow it up to its origin, primarily the distal femur, and down to its insertion, the tendon of Achilles, which then inserts on the calcaneus. This muscle plantar flexes the foot.

2. Examine the lateral surface of the calf, ventral to the gastrocnemius, in order to locate the soleus (Figure 26). This originates on the fibula and then inserts by way of the tendon of Achilles on the calcaneus. It also plantar flexes the foot.

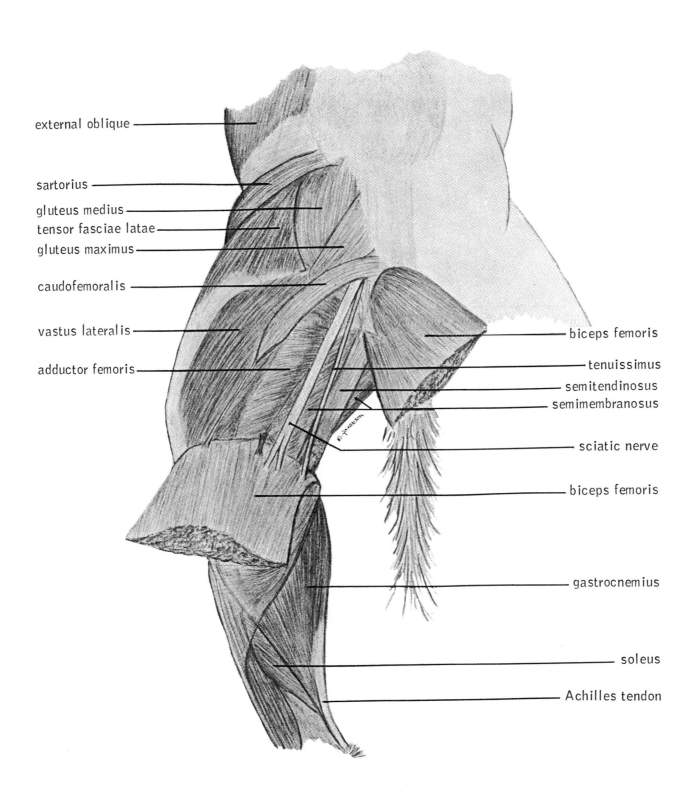

external oblique

sartorius

gluteus medius

tensor fasciae latae

gluteus maximus

caudofemoralis

vastus lateralis

adductor femoris

biceps femoris

tenuissimus

semitendinosus

semimembranosus

sciatic nerve

biceps femoris

gastrocnemius

soleus

Achilles tendon

Figure 26: Deep Muscles of the Dorsal Thigh

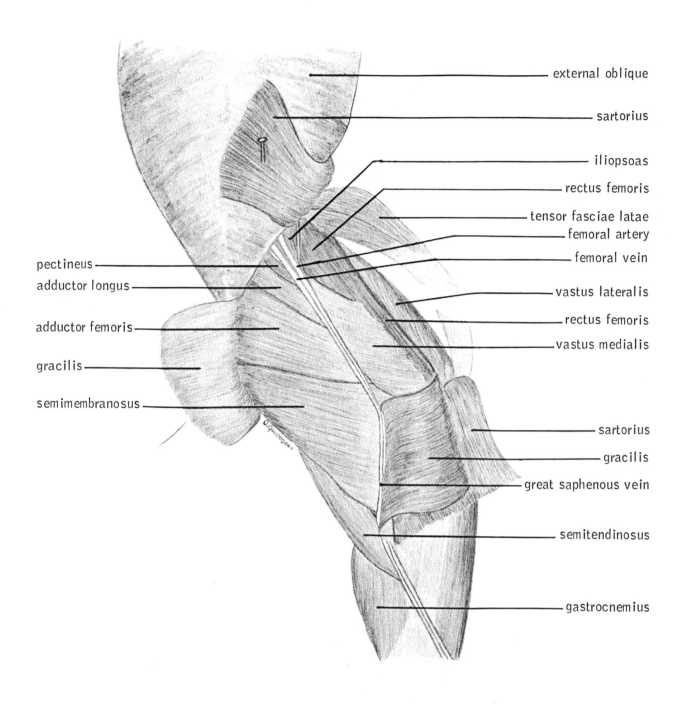

external oblique

sartorius

iliopsoas

rectus femoris

tensor fasciae latae

femoral artery

femoral vein

pectineus

adductor longus

vastus lateralis

rectus femoris

adductor femoris

vastus medialis

gracilis

semimembranosus

sartorius

gracilis

great saphenous vein

semitendinosus

gastrocnemius

Figure 27: Deep View of Ventral Thigh Musculature

40

Part 9. Muscles of the Thorax and Deep Back

PROCEDURE

1. To study the intercostal muscles, raise the posterior border of the origin of the serratus ventralis muscle in order to expose the ribs.

2. The fibers of the external intercostals (Figures 17 and 18) can be seen passing medially and inferiorly between the ribs towards the sternum. The external intercostals lift the ribs in inspiration.

3. Bisect one external intercostal muscle in order to expose the internal intercostals, the fibers of which run at right angles to the external intercostals. These muscles depress the ribs in active expiration.

4. In order to study the deep back muscles, reflect the latissimus dorsi towards its origin. The serratus dorsalis (Figure 17), which consists of a number of short muscle slips, arises from a mid-dorsal aponeurosis and inserts on the ribs. Reflect this muscle by separating it from its origin to expose the sacrospinalis.

5. The sacrospinalis (Figure 18), the muscle which extends the spine and the neck, consists of three longitudinal divisions in the thoracic region. Remove the fascia over this muscle if the subdivisions are not visible. Carefully separate the three divisions. The most lateral, the iliocostalis, lies beneath the serratus dorsalis. It inserts on the ribs. The middle division is called the longissimus dorsi. It fills the space between the spinous and the transverse processes of the thoracic and lumbar vertebrae. In the lumbar region it appears as three separate bundles. The most medial subdivision of the sacrospinalis, the spinalis dorsi, is found next to the spinous processes of the thoracic vertebrae.

Dissection of the Digestive System

The digestive system of the cat is quite similar to that of man. However, there are certain differences that should be noted, such as the absence of the vermiform appendix and the uvula in the cat.

PROCEDURE

1. Locate the major salivary glands of the cat on the left side of the head. If the glands were destroyed during the dissection of the musculature of the head on the left, skin the right side of the head. These glands produce saliva which is carried to the mouth via ducts which pass through the head and neck musculature.

2. The largest salivary gland in the cat is the parotid gland, which is located ventral to the pinna (see Figure 16). This gland can be recognized by its lobular texture. The duct of the parotid crosses the masseter muscle and enters the oral cavity opposite the last upper premolar tooth. Two branches of the facial nerve also cross the masseter dorsal and ventral to the parotid duct.

3. The submandibular gland, which has the same lobular texture as the parotid, lies posterior to the angle of the jaw ventral to the parotid gland (Figure 16). The posterior facial vein passes over this gland. Its duct opens into the floor of the mouth near the lower incisors.

4. The smaller sublingual gland is located anterior to the submandibular gland. Do not confuse this gland with the small lymph node usually located deep to the anterior facial vein and ventral to the submandibular gland (Figure 16).

5. The cat has two additional salivary glands which it is not necessary to locate: the molar gland, which lies near the angle of the mouth, and the infraorbital gland on the floor of the orbit.

6. Open the oral cavity of the cat by cutting with bone shears through the angle of the jaw on each side. Locate the following structures in the oral cavity (see Figure 28): the vestibule, the area lying between the teeth and cheeks; the hard palate, the bony structure containing transverse ridges called the palatine rugae, making up the roof of the mouth; the soft palate, the posterior extension of the hard palate; the fauces, the opening between the oral cavity and the oropharynx; the two small palatine tonsils, masses of lymphatic tissue located on each lateral wall of the pharynx between the glossopalatine arches; the lips; and the labial frenulum, the mucous membrane attached to each lip in the midline.

7. The tongue makes up the floor of the oral cavity. Lift up the tongue in order to locate the lingual frenulum, the mucous membrane which connects the tongue to the floor of the mouth.

8.   Examine the dorsum of the tongue. This surface of the tongue is covered
     with papillae. The filiform papillae, the most numerous type of papillae,
     are pointed - the anterior ones bearing spines with which the cat grooms
     its fur. The filiform papillae are located primarily in the front and middle
     portion of the tongue. Fungiform papillae, which are small, more rounded,
     mushroom shaped papillae, are located between and behind the filiform
     papillae. Four to six large circumvallate (vallate) papillae are located
     near the back of the tongue. Each of these is large and rounded, and sur-
     rounded by a circular groove. Microscopic taste buds are located in the
     depressions between papillae.

9.   Examine the teeth of the cat. The following is the dental formula for the
     cat:

$$\frac{3 - 1 - 3 - 1}{3 - 1 - 2 - 1}$$

10. Slit the soft palate in the midline in order to expose the pharynx. The part
     of the pharynx behind the nasal chamber is the nasopharynx. In the dorsal
     wall of the nasopharynx locate two small slits, the nasal openings of the
     auditory (Eustachian) tubes. The internal nares also open into the naso-
     pharynx.

11. The oropharynx is the part of the pharynx behind the oral cavity. Next
     locate the laryngopharynx, the part of the pharynx behind the larynx. This
     part of the pharynx opens into the larynx and esophagus.

12. Locate the epiglottis, the tonguelike white cartilage over the larynx near the
     root of the tongue. (See Figure 28.)

13. In order to study the remaining digestive organs it is necessary to open
     the body wall. Locate the pubic symphysis. Open the ventral body cavity
     by cutting through the body wall anterior to the pubic symphysis to the base
     of the sternum along the linea alba, being careful not to cut through any in-
     ternal organs. Lift up the origin of the pectoralis group of muscles (so that
     they will not be severed) and continue the incision along the left side of the
     sternum, cutting through the costal cartilages up to the clavicle. Do not
     sever the blood vessels supplying the ventral body wall. Immediately above
     and below the diaphragm make a horizontal incision to each side of the cat.

14. Spread the chest wall so that the heart and lungs are visible. Separate the
     heart and left lung. Locate the esophagus along the dorsal wall of the thoracic
     cavity. The esophagus is the muscular tube connecting the laryngopharynx
     to the stomach. Trace the esophagus down through the diaphragm, the mus-
     cle separating the thoracic cavity from the abdominal cavity.

15. Observe the greater omentum, the apronlike structure containing adipose
     tissue which covers the ventral abdominal organs. (See Figure 29.)

16. The liver is the largest organ in the abdominal cavity. It is the reddish
     brown structure located immediately below the diaphragm. Separate the
     liver from the diaphragm; observe the ligaments of peritoneum attaching
     the liver to the diaphragm and ventral body wall. The ventral ligament is
     the falciform ligament, while the dorsal is the coronary ligament. (See
     Figure 29.)

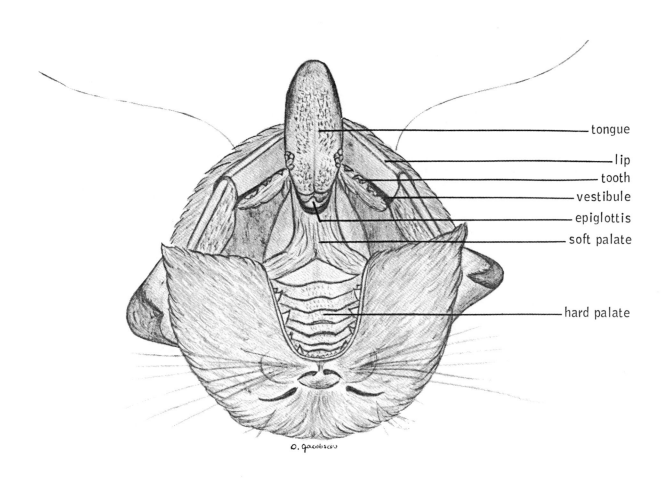

tongue

lip

tooth

vestibule

epiglottis

soft palate

hard palate

Figure 28: Oral Cavity of the Cat

17. The falciform ligament divides the liver into two main lobes, the right and left. Each of these lobes is subdivided into two lobes (lateral and medial). The right lateral lobe, located on the extreme right side of the abdominal cavity behind the right medial lobe, is split into two lobules by a deep cleft. The large left lateral lobe also contains a cleft. In addition there is a small caudate lobe beneath the left lateral lobe and deep to the lesser omentum (Figure 30).

18. Observe the gall bladder in a depression in the large right medial lobe (Figure 29).

19. The stomach lies mainly on the left side of the abdominal cavity. Separate the stomach and liver to observe the esophagus. Locate the point at which the esophagus enters the stomach (see Figure 31). Identify the following regions of the stomach: the cardiac region, adjacent to the point of entrance of the esophagus; the body, the main part of the stomach; the fundus, the dome-shaped portion above the opening of the esophagus; the pyloric region, the most posterior portion of the stomach opening into the duodenum; the greater curvature, the left margin; and the lesser curvature, the right margin.

20. Make a longitudinal incision through the stomach wall beginning in the body and continuing into the duodenum. Wash out the stomach contents. From the interior observe the cardiac sphincter which guards the opening between the esophagus and stomach and the pyloric sphincter, the sphincter between the stomach and duodenum. Note the longitudinal folds called rugae in the wall of the stomach.

21. Locate the spleen, the large organ to the left of the stomach (Figure 31). This structure (part of the circulatory system) is larger in the cat than in man.

22. Lift up the greater omentum, the double layer of peritoneum attaching along the greater curvature of the stomach and to the spleen. The pancreas (Figure 31) lies between the duodenum and the spleen. It can be recognized by its lobular appearance (similar to that of the parotid salivary gland, although it is darker in color). Carefully dissect away part of the pancreas by teasing apart the tissue to locate the pancreatic duct (the Duct of Wirsung) in the interior of the pancreas. This is a white, threadlike duct carrying pancreatic juice to the duodenum. It unites with the common bile duct next to the duodenum forming the ampulla of Vater.

23. Identify the three regions of the small intestine (Figure 31). The duodenum is the C-shaped (U-shaped in the cat) portion attached to the stomach. It is approximately four inches long in the cat. The common bile duct and the pancreatic duct open into the duodenum.

24. The jejunum is the next portion of the small intestine; it makes up about half of the length of this organ. The ileum is the last half of the small intestine, opening into the large intestine. There is no external demarcation between the jejunum and ileum. Open the jejunum or ileum. The velvety appearance in the interior is due to the presence of numerous microscopic villi, which are fingerlike projections that aid in the absorption of food. There may be parasitic roundworms or tape worms present in the small intestine.

25. Trace the small intestine to the point where it enters the large intestine. Observe that the small intestine enters the large intestine about 1/2 inch

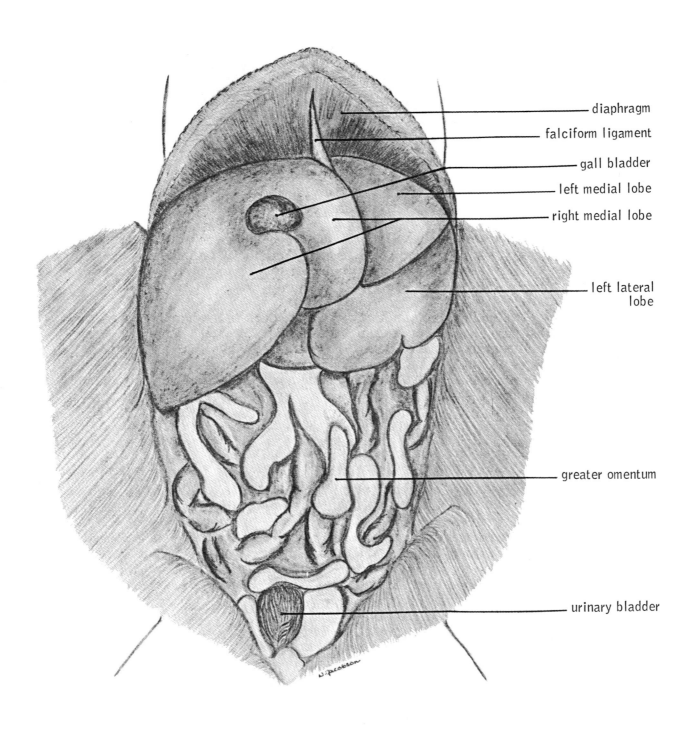

diaphragm

falciform ligament

gall bladder

left medial lobe

right medial lobe

left lateral lobe

greater omentum

urinary bladder

Figure 29: Superficial View of Abdominal Viscera

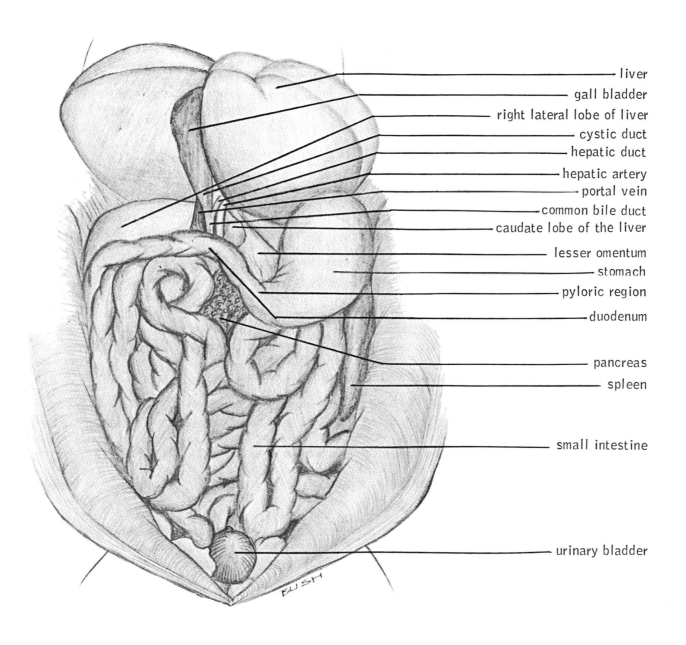

liver
gall bladder
right lateral lobe of liver
cystic duct
hepatic duct
hepatic artery
portal vein
common bile duct
caudate lobe of the liver
lesser omentum
stomach
pyloric region
duodenum

pancreas
spleen

small intestine

urinary bladder

Figure 30: Superficial View of Abdominal Viscera with
Greater Omentum Removed and Liver Raised

47

from the beginning of the large intestine. Locate the ileocecal sphincter between the small and large intestines by making a longitudinal incision through the wall of the colon in the region of the juncture of the two intestines.

26. The portion of the large intestine posterior to the ileocecal valve is the cecum. Observe the posterior end of the cecum. Determine whether an appendix is present. Trace the ascending, transverse, and descending portions of the colon (Figure 31). The ascending colon is on the right side of the abdominal cavity. It extends from the cecum anteriorly to the liver. The transverse colon extends across the abdominal cavity. The descending colon, on the left side of the abdominal cavity, extends in a posterior direction and towards the midline. The next structure, the rectum, then descends down into the pelvic cavity and opens to the outside. The external opening of the rectum is known as the anus.

27. Examine the interior of the abdominal wall. This wall is lined by the parietal peritoneum. The visceral peritoneum covers the abdominal organs inside the abdominal cavity. These two layers are connected by various modifications of the peritoneum.

28. The peritoneum also extends over and between some of the organs in the pelvic cavity. Identify the urinary bladder, the small ventral organ located in the pelvic cavity; the uterus, if your specimen is a female; and the rectum located dorsally in the pelvic cavity.

29. The portion of the abdominal cavity between the urinary bladder and the uterus is called the vesicouterine pouch or excavation. The rectouterine pouch extends between the uterus and rectum. In males the pouch between the large intestine and the urinary bladder is called the rectovesical excavation. These excavations are lined by peritoneum.

30. Identify the modifications of the peritoneum. Observe again the greater omentum. This structure extends from the greater curvature of the stomach and the spleen down over the intestines, folds on itself, and ascends again. Due to its double-layered structure, there is a cavity present called the omental bursa between the ascending and descending layers. To verify this make a small shallow tear in the omentum. A finger can then be inserted between the two layers.

31. The lesser omentum (or gastrohepatoduodenal ligament) can be seen extending from the left lateral lobe of the liver to the stomach and duodenum. Three important vessels are located in the lesser omentum; the common bile duct, the hepatic artery, and the portal vein. Study the location of these ducts in the human as well as in the cat (Figure 30 and 31). Locate the cystic duct coming from the gall bladder and the hepatic duct carrying bile from the liver. These two unite to form the common bile duct. If the ducts contain bile they will be green in color; otherwise, they are colorless and difficult to see. The common bile duct enters the duodenum about 3/4 inch below the pylorus.

32. Carefully tease away the lesser omentum and locate the hepatic artery dorsal and to the left of the common bile duct. This vessel is injected with red latex. In order to locate the portal vein, lift the duodenum and observe the dorsal surface of the lesser omentum and the duodenum. The portal vein is the large vessel entering the liver. It is not injected but has a dark color due to the presence of coagulated blood. As it is thin-walled, it may be damaged during the dissection. A beaded lymphatic vessel may also be seen in this area.

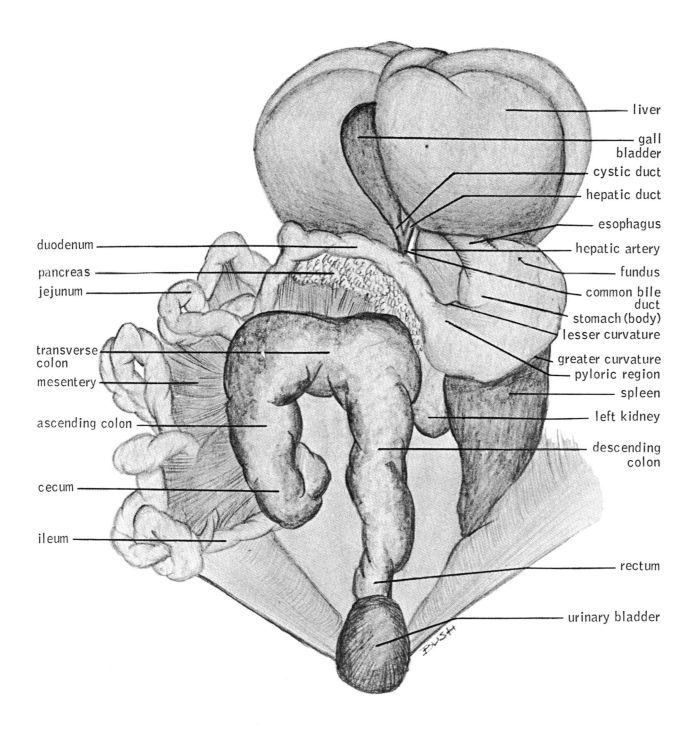

liver

gall
bladder

cystic duct

hepatic duct

esophagus

hepatic artery

fundus

common bile
duct

stomach (body)

lesser curvature

greater curvature

pyloric region

spleen

left kidney

descending
colon

duodenum

pancreas

jejunum

transverse
colon

mesentery

ascending colon

cecum

ileum

rectum

urinary bladder

Figure 31: Abdominal Viscera with Small Intestine and Liver Reflected

33.	Lift up a loop of small intestine and notice that it is connected to the dorsal body wall by a fold of peritoneum called the mesentery (Figure 31). It contains arteries, veins, lymphatic vessels, adipose tissue, and lymph nodes. The lymphatic vessels are not injected and therefore are not easily seen. Feel the mesentery with your fingers to locate the lymph nodes embedded therein. The largest lymph node is called the pancreas of Aselii.

34.	A dorsal mesentery called the mesocolon connects the large intestine to the dorsal body wall. Locate this structure.

35.	Determine which of the organs in the abdominal cavity are retroperitoneal.

Dissection of the Respiratory System

The respiratory systems of the cat and man are very similar. Be prepared to trace the path of air through the respiratory system.

PROCEDURE

1. The mouth and pharynx were examined earlier in the study of the digestive system. The air enters the nasal chamber through the nostrils or external nares, passes on through the internal nares or choanae into the nasopharynx, through the oropharynx, and then the laryngopharynx into the larynx.

2. Clean away the muscles from the ventral surface of the larynx in the neck. The larynx consists of a box of five cartilages. The thyroid cartilage is the large ventral cartilage exposed by the removal of the ventral neck muscles (see Figure 32).

3. Next locate the cricoid cartilage caudal to the thyroid cartilage. This cartilage is shaped like a signet ring with the small band in front, the expanded portion in back.

4. Optional: Locate the two pyramidal-shaped arytenoid cartilages on the dorsal surface of the larynx anterior to the cricoid cartilage. These are visible if the entire larynx is removed. Locate the hyoid bone anterior to the larynx.

5. The epiglottis, the most anterior cartilage of the larynx, has been observed earlier in the dissection of the mouth at the root of the tongue (see Figure 28). This tonguelike cartilage is attached ventrally to the thyroid cartilage.

6. Make a median longitudinal incision through the larynx and upper trachea. Do not sever the blood vessels or nerves located on either side of the trachea. Open the larynx in order to observe the vocal cords. The anterior pair of mucous membranes extending across the larynx are the false vocal cords; the posterior large pair are the true vocal cords. The latter pair extend from the arytenoid cartilages to the thyroid cartilage and are important in the production of sound. The glottis is the space between the true vocal cords (see Figure 32).

7. The trachea leads from the caudal end of the larynx. Observe the large right and left common carotid arteries and tiny internal jugular veins on each side of the trachea. The vagus nerve is the white flattened thread next to the common carotid artery. This nerve supplies many of the thoracic and abdominal organs.

8. Free the trachea laterally from the preceding blood vessels and nerves. Locate the esophagus, the muscular tube dorsal to the trachea.

9. Locate the two small, dark lobes of the thyroid gland, one on each side of the upper trachea near the larynx (Figure 32).

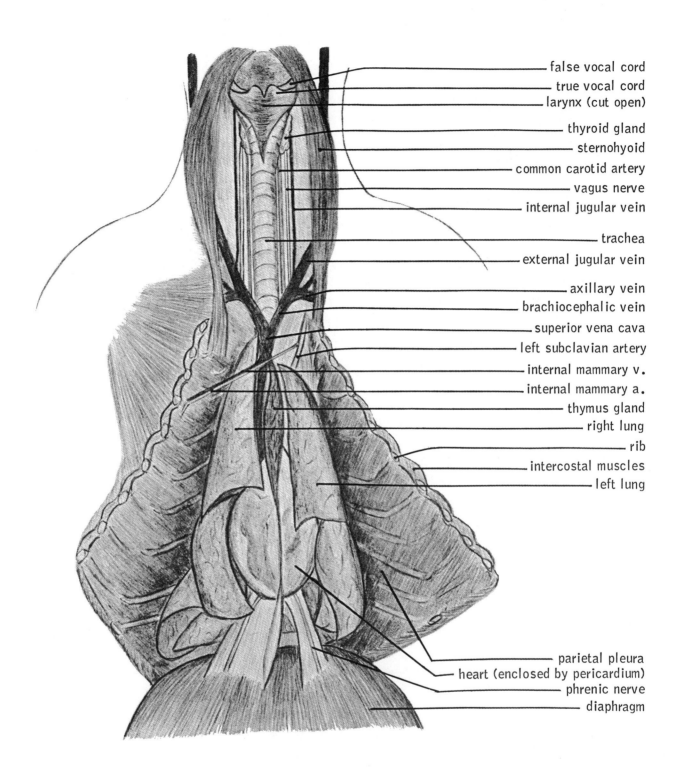

false vocal cord
true vocal cord
larynx (cut open)
thyroid gland
sternohyoid
common carotid artery
vagus nerve
internal jugular vein
trachea
external jugular vein
axillary vein
brachiocephalic vein
superior vena cava
left subclavian artery
internal mammary v.
internal mammary a.
thymus gland
right lung
rib
intercostal muscles
left lung
parietal pleura
heart (enclosed by pericardium)
phrenic nerve
diaphragm

Figure 32: Thoracic Viscera

10. Trace the trachea into the thoracic cavity. Observe the C-shaped rings of cartilage in the wall of the trachea. The rings are completed dorsally by muscle and connective tissue.

11. Examine the interior of the thoracic cavity. Note that the thoracic cavity is divided into two lateral pleural cavities, which contain the lungs. The pericardial sac, which contains the heart, is located in the space between the lungs.

12. The pleura is a double-layered serous membrane which lines the thorax. That portion of the pleura lining the thoracic wall is called the parietal pleura; that which covers and adheres to the lungs is called the visceral pleura.

13. The pericardium, the membrane surrounding the heart is also composed of two layers; the outer parietal layer and the inner visceral layer. Much of the parietal pleura forming the medial walls of the pleural cavities is tightly bound to the parietal pericardium.

14. Examine the lungs. Each lung is divided into lobes. In the cat, the right lung is divided into four lobes and the left lung into three lobes. Cut through a section of the lung in order to observe its internal structures. Many small blood vessels (branches of the pulmonary artery and vein) and tubes (branches of the bronchi) can be seen in the spongy interior.

15. Locate the right and left pulmonary arteries going to the lungs. These are usually injected with blue latex.

16. Note that the lung is attached to other structures in the thorax only by the root. The root of the lung is formed by the bronchus, pulmonary artery and vein, bronchial arteries and veins, nerves, lymphatic vessels, and bronchial lymph nodes, all encircled by pleura.

17. The trachea divides into two bronchi at its posterior end. Lift up the lungs and locate the right and left bronchi. These tubes can be identified by the cartilage in their walls. The bronchi branch repeatedly into secondary bronchi and bronchioles inside the lungs. Scrape away the tissues of the left lung, bit by bit, noting the organization of the bronchial tree and blood vessels. Leave the vessels intact.

18. The mediastinum is the space between the lungs. This space is nearly filled with the heart and pericardium. Locate the thymus gland (Figure 32) in the mediastinum anterior to and ventral to the heart. This gland, divided into lobules, is large in young cats, smaller in old.

19. Examine the interior of the wall of the thoracic cavity. Locate the intercostal vein, artery, and nerve next to each rib.

20. The diaphragm makes up the floor of the thoracic cavity. Locate the phrenic nerves, white threadlike structures directed caudally on each side of the pericardium to the cranial surface of the diaphragm. The phrenic nerves originate from the fifth and sixth cervical nerves.

Dissection of the Circulatory System

The general plan of the circulatory system is much the same in all mammals. However, in the cat observe the differences in the branches of the aortic arch and in the terminal branches of the aorta. Use the diagrams of the cat circulatory system as a guide in your dissection. (Note: there is some variation among cats in the location of the vessels.)

The arteries of the cat have been injected with red latex; the veins with blue. In dissecting the blood vessels, each vein and artery must be freed from adjacent tissues so that it is clearly visible. A probe is most effectively used in freeing the blood vessels from the connective tissues.

Part 1. Dissection of the Veins   (See Figure 33)

PROCEDURE

1. Observe the pericardium surrounding the heart. After determining the structures to which it is attached, remove the parietal layer and the thymus gland. The visceral layer of the pericardium forms the epicardium of the heart.

2. Note that the apex of the heart is directed towards the left. The heart is tilted so that the greater part of the right ventricle lies directly in front, along the ventral surface of the heart. The left ventricle forms the apex of the heart.

3. The atria lie anterior to the ventricles. Each atrium has a conspicuous earlike appendage called the auricle on the ventral surface.

4. A groove, the coronary sulcus, separates the right atrium from the right ventricle. The anterior longitudinal sulcus is the groove that separates the right ventricle from the left ventricle. Dorsal to this sulcus is the interventricular septum. The coronary blood vessels are located in these grooves (the right coronary artery in the coronary sulcus, the left in the anterior longitudinal sulcus). The heart will not be dissected since it is very similar to the sheep heart.

5. Observe the superior vena cava (precaval vein), the large vessel entering the anterior part of the right atrium. This vein drains the head, neck, and arms.

6. Trace this vessel forward and note that it is formed by the union of the two brachiocephalic veins (see Figures 32 and 33).

7. Lift up the heart and the superior vena cava, and carefully dissect away tissue beneath the superior vena cava. The large azygos vein can be seen entering the dorsal surface of the superior vena cava immediately anterior to the heart. Lift up the right lung; the azygos vein is now visible on the right

side against the vertebral column. The tributaries of the azygos vein are the intercostal veins from the body wall, the esophageal veins, and the bronchial veins. It is not necessary to locate the esophageal and bronchial veins.

8. The superior vena cava also receives the internal mammary vein from the ventral chest wall (see Figure 32). The two internal mammary veins unite shortly before they empty into the superior vena cava. The right vertebral vein from the brain also enters the dorsal surface of the superior vena cava.

9. Trace the left brachiocephalic vein forward. This vein receives the left vertebral vein. The brachiocephalic vein is formed by the union of the large superficial left external jugular vein which drains the head and the very short left subclavian vein, which drains the arm.

10. Trace the external jugular vein towards the head. It receives the small internal jugular vein immediately above the point of union of the external jugular with the subclavian. The internal jugular vein, which drains the brain, lies next to the left common carotid artery near the trachea. In man the internal jugular vein is larger than the external jugular vein. The thoracic duct, a large lymphatic vessel, also empties into the external jugular at the point of union of the external jugular with the subclavian. This duct may appear blue if latex was forced into it, or brown and beaded (due to the presence of valves) if it is empty. Continue tracing the external jugular vein towards the head. The large transverse scapular (suprascapular) vein empties into the external jugular.

11. The external jugular vein is formed by the union of the anterior and posterior facial veins under the lower jaw (see Figure 15). The transverse jugular vein can be seen connecting the two external jugular veins at this point.

12. Trace the left subclavian vein through the chest wall. It receives the subscapular vein from the shoulder as it unites with the external jugular. In the axillary region the subclavian is known as the axillary vein. On the arm it becomes the brachial vein.

13. Leave the lungs in position and lift up the heart. Locate the inferior vena cava (postcaval vein) posterior to the heart and trace it forward to the point where it drains into the right atrium. This large vein drains the lower part of the body.

14. Trace the inferior vena cava caudally through the diaphragm into the abdominal cavity where it lies to the right of the aorta. In order to see the vein and its tributaries it will be necessary to dissect away the peritoneum, since the inferior vena cava as well as the aorta is retroperitoneal. The tributaries usually accompany the arteries of the same name.

15. The hepatic veins drain blood from the liver into the inferior vena cava. To locate these veins, gently scrape away tissue on the right anterior surface of the liver. Several hepatic veins may be located in this manner.

16. The adrenolumbar veins drain the adrenal glands and body wall. The right adrenolumbar vein drains into the inferior vena cava, the left drains into the renal vein. These veins may be located by examining the muscle dorsal to the kidney.

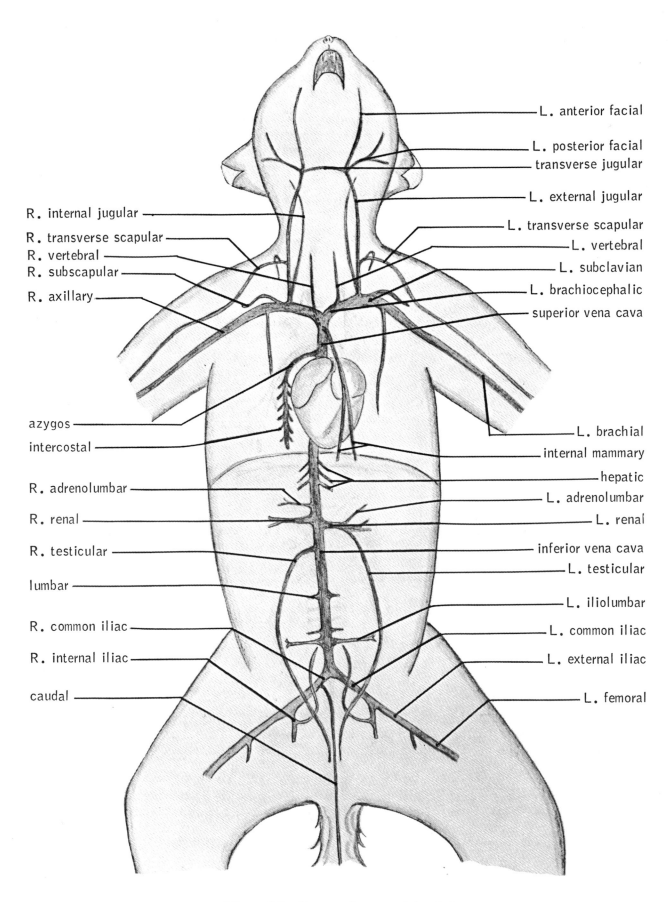

L. anterior facial

L. posterior facial

transverse jugular

L. external jugular

R. internal jugular

L. transverse scapular

R. transverse scapular

L. vertebral

R. vertebral

L. subclavian

R. subscapular

L. brachiocephalic

R. axillary

superior vena cava

azygos

L. brachial

intercostal

internal mammary

hepatic

R. adrenolumbar

L. adrenolumbar

R. renal

L. renal

R. testicular

inferior vena cava

L. testicular

lumbar

L. iliolumbar

R. common iliac

L. common iliac

R. internal iliac

L. external iliac

caudal

L. femoral

Figure 33: Venous System of the Cat

56

17. Locate the renal veins, which carry blood from the kidneys into the inferior vena cava. The right renal vein may be multiple. Note that the right renal vein is higher than the left.

18. Below the renals are the long thin paired ovarian or testicular veins. They are most easily located by tracing the vessels from the gonads back towards the inferior vena cava. If the cat is a female, locate the ovaries, small oval bodies near the cranial ends of the uterus, below the kidneys. The ovarian artery and vein should now be visible. If the cat is a male, the internal spermatic (testicular) vein, artery, and vas deferens can be seen passing through the inguinal canal (the opening in the posterior abdominal wall). Trace these blood vessels cranially towards the aorta and inferior vena cava. The left testicular vein enters the renal vein in the cat, the right enters the inferior vena cava.

19. Several pairs of lumbar veins enter the dorsal surface of the inferior vena cava at intervals in the abdominal cavity. The larger right and left ilio-lumbar veins enter the inferior vena cava near the base. These vessels drain the abdominal wall muscles.

20. Observe the great saphenous vein on the lower thigh and leg if it was not removed in skinning the cat. Trace it forward until it drains into the femoral vein, the superficial vein on the anterior surface of the thigh between the gracilis and sartorius muscles. Trace the femoral vein anteriorly until it passes beneath the posterior border of the external oblique muscle.

21. As the femoral vein disappears beneath the external oblique muscle it becomes the external iliac vein. The external iliac is very short, as immediately above the body wall it receives the internal iliac vein, which drains the rectum, bladder, and internal reproductive organs, and becomes the common iliac vein. Trace the right and left common iliac veins anteriorly until they unite to form the inferior vena cava.

22. The portal system is usually not injected in cats, so it will not be necessary to dissect the smaller veins. The portal vein (hepatic portal vein) has been dissected earlier with the digestive system (see Figure 30). The portal vein and its tributaries drain the digestive organs and carry the blood to the liver. Follow the portal vein caudally. It is formed by the union of the gastrosplenic vein coming from the stomach and spleen, and the larger superior mesenteric vein coming in posteriorly from the intestines and the pancreas.

Part 2. Dissection of the Arteries   (See Figure 34)

PROCEDURE

1. Locate the pulmonary artery on the ventral surface of the heart. Trace it down to its origin in the right ventricle; then follow it towards the lungs, noting that it branches into a right and left pulmonary artery.

2. Push aside the right auricle. The large white vessel that can be seen emerging from the left ventricle and passing beneath the pulmonary artery is the aorta (dorsal aorta). This is injected with red latex, but due to the thickness of the wall of the aorta the color often cannot be seen. (Do not remove the wall of the aorta in your dissection.)

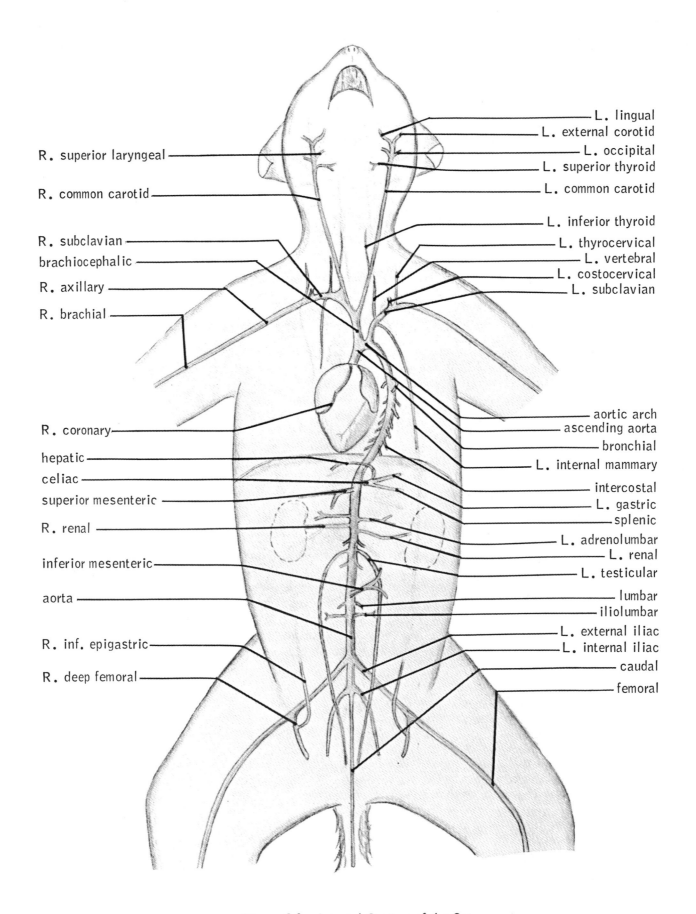

R. superior laryngeal

R. common carotid

R. subclavian
brachiocephalic
R. axillary
R. brachial

R. coronary

hepatic
celiac
superior mesenteric

R. renal

inferior mesenteric

aorta

R. inf. epigastric

R. deep femoral

L. lingual
L. external corotid
L. occipital
L. superior thyroid
L. common carotid

L. inferior thyroid
L. thyrocervical
L. vertebral
L. costocervical
L. subclavian

aortic arch
ascending aorta
bronchial
L. internal mammary
intercostal
L. gastric
splenic
L. adrenolumbar
L. renal
L. testicular
lumbar
iliolumbar
L. external iliac
L. internal iliac
caudal
femoral

Figure 34: Arterial System of the Cat

3. Dissect away the base of the ascending aorta until the right and left coronary arteries are visible. These arise just anterior to the aortic semilunar valve. The right coronary artery can then be seen in the coronary sulcus on the surface of the heart; the left coronary artery in the anterior longitudinal sulcus.

4. The dorsal aorta passes anteriorly for a short distance and then turns to the left. This region of the aorta is called the aortic arch. Two large arteries originate from the aortic arch. The first branch is the brachiocephalic artery. Trace this vessel forward. The brachiocephalic gives off first the left common carotid artery and then branches into the right subclavian and the right common carotid arteries. The left subclavian artery leaves the arch separately.

5. Trace the left common carotid artery. It ascends in the neck, lying between the tiny internal jugular vein and trachea. The first branch of the left common carotid artery is the inferior thyroid artery. This runs anteriorly along the trachea. The superior thyroid artery originates at the level of the thyroid cartilage. It supplies the thyroid gland and some of the neck musculature. Anterior to this is the occipital artery which supplies the back of the neck.

6. The left common carotid branches to form the external and internal carotid arteries at the anterior border of the larynx. The internal carotid is very small in the cat and need not be located. It passes dorsally to enter the skull. The larger external carotid artery continues on to supply the external structures of the head.

7. Returning to the aortic arch, locate the left subclavian artery, which supplies the left side of the chest and the left arm. Trace along the left subclavian artery. The internal mammary artery branches from the ventral surface of the subclavian and passes to the ventral thoracic wall where it accompanies the corresponding vein.

8. The vertebral artery arises from the dorsal surface of the subclavian artery nearly opposite the internal mammary artery. This passes cranially and supplies the brain. The next branch of the subclavian artery is the costo-cervical trunk. This supplies some of the neck, back, and intercostal muscles. Locate next the thyrocervical trunk, which ascends for a short distance and then branches. It also supplies some of the neck and shoulder muscles.

9. The subclavian artery becomes the axillary artery as it emerges from the chest cavity and crosses the axillary space. It continues into the arm where it is known as the brachial artery. Follow the brachial artery until it branches to form the radial and ulnar arteries which supply the forearm.

10. Returning to the aortic arch, trace the aorta caudally. Pull the viscera in the thorax to the right to expose the aorta in the thoracic cavity. As this vessel passes through the thorax it is called the thoracic aorta. Remove the pleura to expose this vessel in the thorax.

11. Note the intercostal arteries emerging from the thoracic aorta. These supply the intercostal muscles. There are also, branching from the thoracic aorta, several bronchial arteries which supply the lungs and esophageal arteries which supply the esophagus.

12. Trace the descending aorta through the diaphragm. The first major branch from the abdominal aorta is the short celiac artery. In order to locate this artery it is necessary to remove the peritoneum covering the anterior end of the abdominal aorta immediately beneath the diaphragm. The celiac artery divides into three branches: hepatic, left gastric, and splenic. The hepatic artery was located earlier in the lesser omentum to the left of the portal vein during the dissection of the digestive system (see Figure 30). Trace the hepatic artery from the celiac artery under the stomach to the liver. Locate the cystic artery, a branch of the hepatic artery, which supplies the gall bladder. The left gastric artery runs directly to the lesser curvature of the stomach and then branches to supply the stomach. The splenic artery is the largest branch of the celiac. Trace this to the spleen.

13. Locate the superior mesenteric artery, the unpaired vessel posterior to the celiac artery. This vessel is also retroperitoneal. It supplies the small intestine and a portion of the large intestine.

14. The paired adrenolumbar arteries run from the aorta to the dorsal body wall. They supply the adrenal glands, diaphragm, and muscles of the body wall.

15. Observe the renal arteries posterior to the superior mesenteric artery. These arteries supply the kidney.

16. The right and left genital arteries are small threadlike vessels that emerge from the ventral surface of the aorta posterior to the renals. If your specimen is a male, follow the testicular (internal spermatic) arteries from the inguinal canal to the aorta. The testicular artery supplies the testis. If your specimen is a female, trace the ovarian artery to the ovary. This vessel supplies the uterus as well as the ovary.

17. Push the descending colon to one side to see the unpaired inferior mesenteric artery. This arises from the aorta posterior to the ovarian or testicular arteries. It divides almost immediately, with one branch (the left colic artery) proceeding anteriorly, and one branch (the superior hemorrhoidal) posteriorly along the dorsal surface of the colon.

18. The cat has approximately seven pairs of lumbar arteries emerging at intervals along the abdominal aorta. These supply the abdominal wall. A larger pair of arteries, the iliolumbars, may be seen just above the termination of the aorta running laterally to the body wall.

19. Observe carefully the base of the aorta (see Figure 34). There is no common iliac artery in the cat. Instead, the paired external iliac arteries arise from the aorta, and then the paired internal iliac arteries arise independently from the aorta. The branches of the internal iliac supply the gluteal muscles, rectum, and uterus. As the external iliac artery passes through the body wall, it becomes the femoral artery. Trace this vessel down the ventral surface of the thigh.

20. After giving off the iliac arteries, the aorta continues as the caudal or median sacral artery. It travels down the median ventral surface of the sacrum and enters the tail.

Dissection of the Sheep Heart

The anatomy of the sheep heart is very similar to that of the human and the cat. Observe carefully in this exercise the remnants of structures important in fetal circulation. Directions for this exercise are given with the heart in anatomic position.

PROCEDURE

1. Rinse the sheep heart in water to remove as much preservative as possible.

2. The pericardium (the fibro-serous membrane surrounding the heart) has been largely removed in preparing the sheep heart. Observe the remnants of this membrane attached to the large blood vessels above the heart.

3. Separate a small portion of the epicardium (the visceral layer of the pericardium) from the myocardium by careful dissection with a scalpel. The third layer of the heart, the endocardium, will be visible when the heart is opened.

4. Locate the pulmonary artery on the ventral surface of the heart. This artery emerges from the anterior ventral surface of the heart, medial to the left auricle. (To determine which is the ventral surface of the heart, compare the sheep heart with Figure 35.)

5. Note the anterior longitudinal sulcus separating the right ventricle from the left ventricle. The coronary blood vessels can be seen in this sulcus.

6. Compare the thickness of the wall of the right ventricle with the left ventricle by pressing the wall of each ventricle between your thumb and forefinger.

7. If there is a demonstration dissected sheep heart on display, observe the incisions before proceeding. Using great care, make a shallow incision through the ventral wall of the pulmonary artery and the right ventricle parallel to, and 3/4 of an inch to the right of the anterior longitudinal sulcus. Do not dissect so deeply that you cut into the dorsal surface of either the pulmonary artery or right ventricle. Continue the incision forward anteriorly to the point where the pulmonary artery branches into the right and left pulmonary arteries. Remove as much adipose tissue as necessary to expose the branches of the pulmonary artery.

8. Open the pulmonary artery and note the pulmonary semilunar valve. Observe the number of pouches in this valve. Remove any coagulated blood present in the blood vessels or heart.

9. Continue the original incision through the right ventricle wall (keeping parallel to the anterior longitudinal sulcus) around and through the dorsal wall of the right ventricle until reaching the interventricular septum.

10. Examine the dorsal surface of the heart. The thin-walled superior vena cava can be seen above the right auricle, extending straight down into the

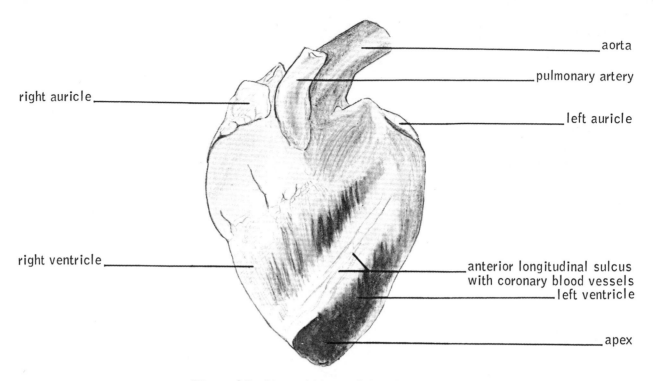

right auricle

aorta

pulmonary artery

left auricle

right ventricle

anterior longitudinal sulcus
with coronary blood vessels

left ventricle

apex

Figure 35: Ventral View of the Sheep Heart

right atrium. Make a longitudinal incision through the dorsal wall of the superior vena cava, continuing down through the right atrium (immediately to the left of the right auricle). Continue this incision down the dorsal right ventricle wall to the point of juncture with the first incision.

11. If the incisions were properly made, it should now be possible to spread open the superior vena cava, right atrium, and right ventricle. Compare your dissection with Figure 36.

12. Determine whether there is a valve present at the entrance of the superior vena cava into the right atrium.

13. Observe the internal structure of the right auricle. The muscle visible in the interior of the auricle is called the pectinate muscle, since it resembles a comb (pecten).

14. Locate the large opening of the inferior vena cava on the left side of the interior of the right atrium. Insert a finger or probe through the mouth of this vein in order to locate the external opening on the dorsal surface of the heart. Compare the location of this vein with the corresponding vein in humans.

15. Locate the orifice of the coronary sinus posterior to the opening of the inferior vena cava. Locate this vessel on the dorsal surface of the heart.

16. Locate the interatrial septum, the wall that separates the two atria. Examine this septum from the interior of the right atrium. Locate the fossa ovalis, the oval-shaped depression, ventral to the entrance of the inferior vena cava.

17. Examine the tricuspid valve between the right atrium and the right ventricle. Determine the number of cusps that form this valve.

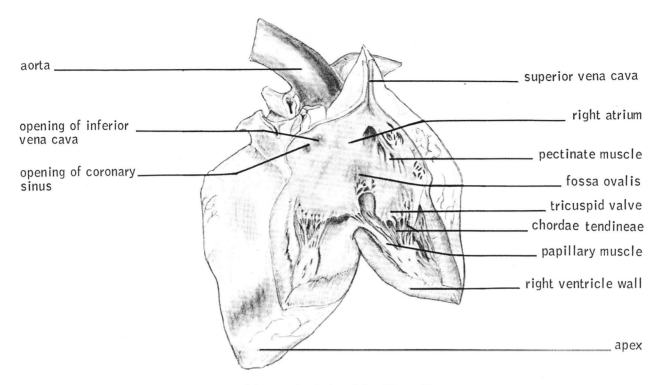

aorta

opening of inferior vena cava

opening of coronary sinus

superior vena cava

right atrium

pectinate muscle

fossa ovalis

tricuspid valve

chordae tendineae

papillary muscle

right ventricle wall

apex

Figure 36: Right Side of the Sheep Heart

18. Locate the papillary muscles and chordae tendineae in the wall of the right ventricle. Determine the number of papillary muscles.

19. Locate the moderator band crossing the lumen of the right ventricle. This is believed to prevent overdistension of the ventricle.

20. Try to locate the four pulmonary veins entering the left atrium. These vessels are visible on the dorsal surface of the left atrium. Whether the four vessels can be located depends on how they were cut.

21. Locate the most lateral of the pulmonary veins. Make a longitudinal incision through this pulmonary vein. Continue this incision down through the wall of the left atrium and the left ventricle to the apex of the heart.

22. Spread open the left side of the heart. Compare the wall thickness of the left ventricle with that of the right.

23. Observe the bicuspid valve. Determine how many major cusps comprise this valve. Determine which of the following are present in the left ventricle: moderator band, chordae tendineae, papillary muscles.

24. Insert a finger up along the midline of the left ventricle into the aorta. Cut carefully along this line until the aortic semilunar valve is visible. Count the number of pouches in this valve.

25. Returning to the external surface of the heart, locate the thick-walled aorta above the heart, arching to the left. Locate the brachiocephalic artery which branches from the aortic arch. This vessel later branches into the subclavian and common carotid arteries, which supply the arms and head. In humans, three large blood vessels branch from the aortic arch.

26. Open the aorta as it emerges from the network of blood vessels anterior to the heart. Observe the smooth lining of this vessel.

27. If the pulmonary artery and the aorta have not been severed too close to the heart when removing the heart from the sheep, you will be able to locate the ligamentum arteriosum, the remnant of the ductus arteriosus. Carefully dissect away the adipose tissue between the pulmonary artery and the aorta anterior to the heart. Be careful not to sever the ligamentum arteriosum when removing the adipose tissue.

Dissection of the Sheep Brain

The structure of the sheep brain is very similar to that of the human and cat brains. Note any differences as you study the brains. The brain is surrounded by three layers of <u>meninges</u>. The outermost, the <u>dura mater</u>, was removed in preparing the sheep brains. This layer may be seen surrounding the brain of the cat if the surrounding cranial bones are carefully cut away with scissors.

PROCEDURE

1. Obtain a sagittal section of the sheep brain and an entire sheep brain and rinse both with tap water.

2. The inner two layers of the meninges can be seen covering the brain. The <u>arachnoid</u>, the middle layer, lies between the <u>dura mater</u> and the <u>pia mater</u>, the innermost, vascular layer of the meninges. The arachnoid is most easily distinguished from the pia mater in the region overlying the grooves on the brain surface, since the pia mater dips into the grooves and the arachnoid does not.

3. Observe the anterior paired <u>cerebral hemispheres</u> and the posterior <u>cerebellum</u> on the dorsal surface of the brain. The cerebral hemispheres are separated from each other by the <u>longitudinal fissure</u>; the cerebellum is separated from the cerebral hemispheres by the <u>transverse fissure</u> (see Figure 37).

4. Spread the cerebral hemispheres apart and observe deep in the longitudinal fissure the thick transverse band of fibers, the <u>corpus callosum</u>, that connects the cerebral hemispheres.

5. The surface of each hemisphere is composed of numerous convolutions. The raised area of each convolution is called the <u>gyrus</u>, the depression a <u>sulcus</u>.

6. The roof of the midbrain (mesencephalon) can be seen by spreading the cerebral hemispheres and cerebellum apart (see Figure 37). Four prominent round swellings, the <u>corpora quadrigemina</u>, form the roof of the midbrain. The larger, anterior pair is called the <u>superior colliculi</u>, the smaller, posterior pair the <u>inferior colliculi</u>. The <u>pineal body</u> can be seen between the superior colliculi. The <u>trochlear nerve</u> appears as a thin, white strand, directed ventrally, slightly posterior to the inferior colliculi.

7. Posterior to the cerebral hemispheres is the <u>cerebellum</u>. The cerebellum is connected with the brain stem by three prominent fiber tracts or peduncles. Lift up the lateral edge of the cerebellum. The middle cerebellar <u>peduncle</u> can be seen connecting the cerebellum with the pons. Slightly posterior to this is the <u>inferior cerebellar peduncle</u> connecting the cerebellum to the medulla. Locate the <u>superior cerebellar peduncle</u>, which is composed of the fibers connecting the midbrain to the cerebellum.

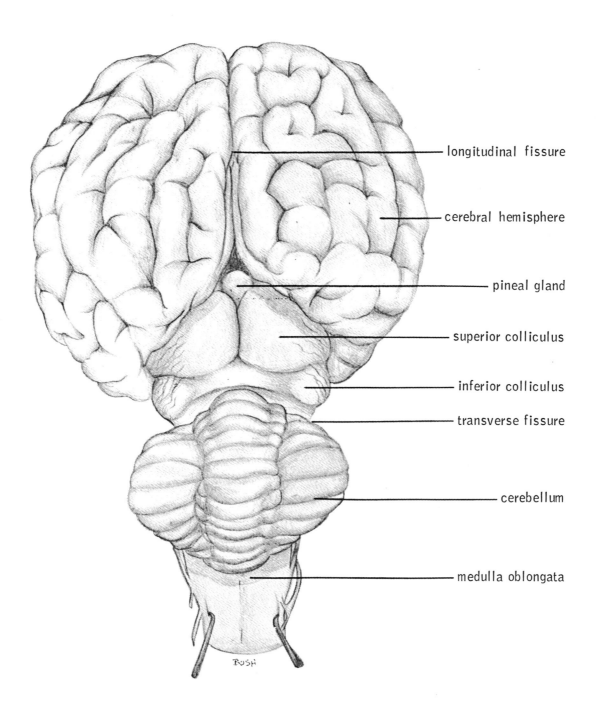

longitudinal fissure

cerebral hemisphere

pineal gland

superior colliculus

inferior colliculus

transverse fissure

cerebellum

medulla oblongata

Figure 37: Dorsal View of Sheep Brain
(with cerebellum separated from
cerebral hemispheres)

8. Observe the ventral surface of the sheep brain. A pair of olfactory bulbs can be seen beneath the cerebral hemispheres. These bulbs lie over the cribriform plate of the ethmoid and receive the olfactory neurons from the nose (see Figure 38).

9. A white band, the olfactory tract, extends from each bulb along the ventral surface of the cerebral hemispheres.

10. The ventral surface of the diencephalon, the hypothalamus, is posterior to the olfactory tracts. The optic nerves undergo a partial crossing over (decussation) at the anterior border of the hypothalamus, forming the cross known as the optic chiasma.

11. The remainder of the hypothalamus is the oval area lying posterior to the optic chiasma, covered by the pituitary gland (hypophysis). Do not remove the gland. The infundibulum can be seen connecting the pituitary to the hypothalamus.

12. Posterior to the infundibulum is the rounded mammillary body (there are two in humans).

13. Observe the cerebral peduncles on the ventral surface of the midbrain. The large oculomotor nerves, covered by the pituitary gland, arise from the cerebral peduncles posterior to the mammillary body.

14. Posterior to the midbrain is the pons. This is composed primarily of white fibers, many of which run transversely across the pons out to the cerebellum.

15. The medulla oblongata is posterior to the pons. The longitudinal bands of tissue at each side of the ventral median fissure on the ventral surface of the medulla are known as the pyramids.

16. To see the remaining parts of the brain, use the sagittal section of the sheep brain. (Compare the specimen with Figure 39, sagittal section of the sheep brain.) Relocate the corpus callosum, which consists of the white fibers connecting the two cerebral hemispheres.

17. A thin, vertical septum of tissue, the septum pellucidum, lies ventral to the corpus callosum. The lateral ventricle lies behind this septum and may be seen by breaking the septum.

18. The fornix, a band of white fibers, lies ventral to the septum.

19. The third ventricle and the thalamus lie ventral to the fornix. The narrow third ventricle, the walls of which are covered by a shiny layer of epithelium, is in the midline. The thalamus forms the lateral walls of the third ventricle.

20. The massa intermedia extends across the third ventricle, connecting the two sides of the thalamus. This structure appears as a dull circular area not covered by the epithelium.

21. The foramen of Monro, the opening through which each lateral ventricle communicates with the third ventricle, lies in the depression anterior to the massa intermedia. Find this connection by passing a dull probe through it.

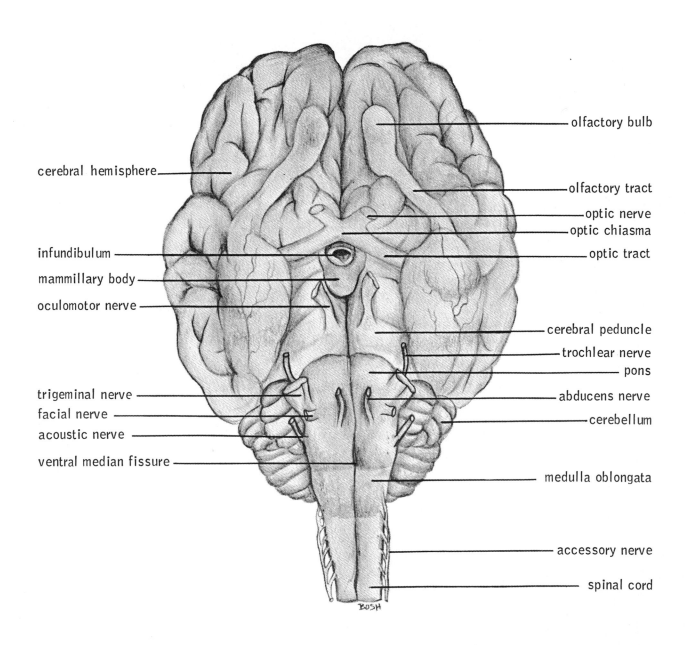

cerebral hemisphere

infundibulum
mammillary body
oculomotor nerve

trigeminal nerve
facial nerve
acoustic nerve
ventral median fissure

olfactory bulb

olfactory tract
optic nerve
optic chiasma
optic tract

cerebral peduncle
trochlear nerve
pons
abducens nerve
cerebellum

medulla oblongata

accessory nerve
spinal cord

BOSH

Figure 38: Ventral View of Sheep Brain

68

22. Relocate the <u>hypothalamus</u>. This lies ventral to the third ventricle.

23. Note the <u>pineal body</u> dorsal to the midbrain, near the <u>superior colliculus</u>.

24. Observe the narrow <u>cerebral aqueduct</u> leading through the midbrain, connecting the third and <u>fourth ventricles</u>.

25. The <u>fourth ventricle</u> lies above the pons and medulla, below the cerebellum.

26. The beginning of the spinal cord may be seen connected to the medulla. A canal known as the <u>central canal</u>, which is connected to the fourth ventricle, is present in the center of the cord.

27. Note the treelike arrangement of gray and white matter in the cerebellum. This arrangement is known as the <u>arbor vitae</u> (tree of life). The gray matter of the cerebellum is on the outside, the white is toward the center.

28. The outer layer of the cerebral hemispheres, the <u>cortex</u>, is also composed of gray matter. Make a shallow incision through the cortex in order to see the white matter located beneath.

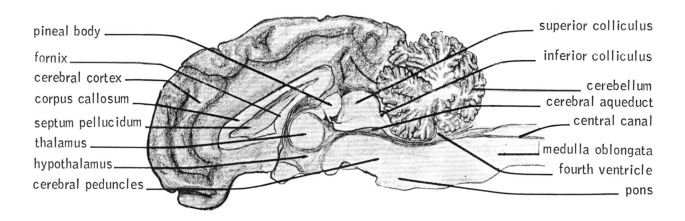

Figure 39: Sagittal Section through Sheep Brain

Dissection of the Cat Brain

1. The cat brain is very similar in structure to the sheep brain. Remove the muscles from the top and sides of the skull.

2. Using either bone shears or a bone saw, make an opening in the parietal bones. Carefully chip away bone from the sides of this opening until the brain is completely exposed.

3. Remove the transverse bony septum that extends between the cerebellum and the cerebral hemispheres.

4. Separate the spinal cord from the medulla at the foramen magnum.

5. Lift the brain carefully out of the cranial cavity, severing each cranial nerve as far from the brain as possible.

6. Remove the dura mater; then follow steps 2-28 of the procedure for the sheep brain.

Dissection of the Cat Peripheral Nervous System

There are 38 pairs of spinal nerves in the cat. There are usually eight cervical, thirteen thoracic, seven lumbar, three sacral and seven caudal nerves. Each spinal nerve emerges from the spinal cord through the intervertebral foramen and divides to form two rami, dorsal and ventral. The ventral rami form the major plexuses which supply the arms and legs as well as the skin and musculature of the ventral trunk. The dorsal rami are smaller and supply only the skin and musculature of the back. Only a few of the major nerves will be identified. Many of these have been located previously in the dissection of the cat muscular and respiratory systems.

PROCEDURE

1. The first four cervical nerves supply the lateral neck musculature. It is not necessary to locate these nerves.

2. The phrenic nerve has been identified earlier in the dissection of the respiratory system (see Figure 32). The two phrenic nerves are formed by the 5th and 6th cervical nerves; they pass lateral to the heart on their way to the diaphragm.

3. The 6th through 8th cervical nerves and 1st thoracic nerve form the brachial plexus which supplies the muscles of the arm. This plexus has been exposed during the dissection of the chest and arm muscles (see Figure 19). If this plexus was severed on the left side during the dissection of the muscles, cut carefully through the pectoralis group on the right side of the chest until it is reached.

   a. The most anterior nerve of the brachial plexus is the musculocutaneous nerve. This small nerve may be identified as it passes along the lower edge of the biceps brachii muscle. This nerve supplies the biceps, coracobrachialis, and brachialis muscles.

   b. The large nerve dorsal and anterior to the brachial artery, passing between the triceps and the humerus, is the radial nerve, the largest nerve of the plexus. Follow this nerve to the dorsal surface of the upper arm and trace it to the forearm. This splits in two near the elbow.

   c. Raise the anterior portion of the plexus. A Y-shaped formation can be observed anterior to the teres major muscle at the lateral border of the scapula. This is the median nerve. It passes with the brachial artery (anterior to the artery) to the elbow region, through the supracondyloid foramen in the humerus, to the forearm. This foramen is not present in humans.

   d. The ulnar nerve is the most posterior nerve of the important arm nerves. It emerges from the medial fork of the Y, runs posterior to the brachial artery down to the wrist. It passes between the medial epicondyle of the humerus and the olecranon process of the ulna at the elbow.

4. The next twelve thoracic nerves pass between the ribs with an artery and vein. They are known here as the intercostal nerves, arteries and veins. The nerves supply the intercostal muscles.

5. The <u>sciatic</u> <u>nerve</u> is the major nerve emerging from the <u>lumbosacral</u> <u>plexus</u>. This plexus is made up of the last four lumbar nerves and the three sacral nerves. Locate the sciatic nerve beneath the biceps femoris muscle (see Figure 26). Trace it to the popliteal fossa where it divides into two branches which supply the leg.

6. The <u>femoral</u> <u>nerve</u> also emerges from the lumbosacral plexus. This nerve is located on the ventral surface of the thigh with the femoral artery between the gracilis and sartorius muscles.

7. The larger cranial nerves have been identified in the dissection of the cat and sheep brain.

8. The autonomic nervous system of the cat will not be dissected. It is possible to observe (in the thoracic cavity) without dissection the two <u>sympathetic</u> <u>trunks</u>, located one on each side of the veretebral column. Push the left <u>lung</u> to the right and locate the sympathetic trunks on the dorsal wall of the thoracic cavity. The sympathetic trunks are beneath the parietal pleura parallel to the vertebral column. They resemble white threads.

Dissection of the Sheep Eye

The size and structures of the sheep eye compare favorably with that of the human eye. This, coupled with their availability, makes them ideal for studying the anatomical structures of the eye.

PROCEDURE

1. Note the fat on the surface of the eye. This cushions the eye from shock in its bony orbit.

2. Identify the following structures:

   a. The sclera, the tough, external, white coat.

   b. The conjunctiva, reflected over the anterior surface of the eye and attached to the eyeball a short distance from the edge of the cornea.

   c. The cornea, the anterior, transparent (opaque in your specimen, due to action of the preservative), portion of the sclera.

   d. The optic nerve, located on the posterior surface. The nerve has the appearance of a solid white core and is approximately 3 mm thick.

3. Carefully dissect away the connective tissue (fat, etc.) from the posterior surface of the eyeball to free the six extrinsic eye muscles. These resemble flattened straps.

4. Hold the eye so that the cornea is in an inferior position.

5. Making an incision into the eyeball about 1/2 cm from the edge of the cornea, cut completely around the eye (parallel to the cornea).

6. If the incision was made properly, it should now be possible to carefully separate the vitreous humor (vitreous body) from the crystalline lens, and to keep the vitreous humor in the posterior portion of the eyeball, the lens in the anterior third of the eye.

7. Examine the interior of the anterior part of the eye.

   a. Observe the ciliary body, the black structure which has the appearance of narrow, radial folds.

   b. Locate the suspensory ligaments, the very delicate fibers connecting the ciliary body to the lens. They hold the lens in position.

   c. Free the lens from the ciliary body and remove it. Remnants of the suspensory ligaments can be seen attached to the lens.

   d. The iris is now visible anterior to the former position of the lens. This also appears black. Try to distinguish between the circular and radial fibers comprising the iris.

   e. Hold the lens up to the light. Does any light pass through? The lens in your specimen may be opaque due to the action of the preservative.

8. Examine the external surface of the anterior third of the eye. It is now relatively easy to distinguish the iris, pupil, and cornea.

9. Examine the posterior two-thirds of the eye and observe the following structures:

   a. The vitreous humor (in life, this substance is perfectly clear). Remove it from the eyeball.

   b. The retina, the white inner coat that was covered by the vitreous humor. Determine the point at which the retina is attached dorsally.

   c. The choroid coat. The retina covers this coat, and the two are easily separated. The iridescent appearance of the choroid is due to the presence of the tapetum lucidum, a special structure not present in the human eye. The function of the tapetum lucidum is to reflect some light back onto the retina. This reflecting device is found in vertebrates that live under conditions of low light intensity. This causes the animal's eyes to shine in the dark.

   d. The sclera, the outer, white coat.

Dissection of the Urinary System

The organs in the urinary system of the cat are very similar to those in the human. As you dissect the organs, be prepared to trace the path of urine from its site of production to the point at which it passes to the outside. The cat kidney will be sectioned in order to study its internal structure, since it provides a good example of a typical mammalian kidney.

PROCEDURE

1. Opposite the last thoracic and first three lumbar vertebrae, observe the large bean-shaped kidneys on the dorsal body wall of the cat. Use Figure 40 as a guide. Each kidney is surrounded by adipose tissue (perirenal fat). The right kidney is higher in position than the left.

2. Remove the adipose tissue and the peritoneum, which covers the ventral surface of the kidney, from the left kidney. Since the kidneys are separated from the abdominal organs by a layer of peritoneum, their location is described as being retroperitoneal.

3. Identify the renal artery and renal vein, which carry blood to and from the kidney.

4. Locate the small adrenal glands lying in the connective tissue close to the aorta and just anterior and medial to each kidney. The adrenal glands resemble small lymph nodes in the cat (see Figure 40).

5. Observe the ureter, the narrow, white, convoluted tube which drains the urine from each kidney. Trace the ureter from the hilus, the opening on the medial border of each kidney, freeing it from the peritoneum. The ureters pass behind the urinary bladder to open into the floor of the bladder.

6. The pear-shaped urinary bladder is connected to the mid-ventral wall by a median suspensory ligament and to the lateral walls by lateral ligaments, which contain a large amount of adipose tissue.

7. The fundus is the large expanded part of the bladder. The neck is the lower part which opens into the urethra.

8. Locate the urethra, the duct which conducts urine from the posterior end of the bladder to the outside. The remainder of the urethra will be freed when the reproductive system is dissected.

9. Remove the left kidney and make a longitudinal (coronal) section through it. Locate each of the following structures. (See Figure 41.)

   a. The renal capsule is the thin layer of connective tissue around the outside of the kidney.

   b. The renal cortex is the outer light brown layer of the kidney immediately beneath the capsule. This layer contains renal corpuscles.

75

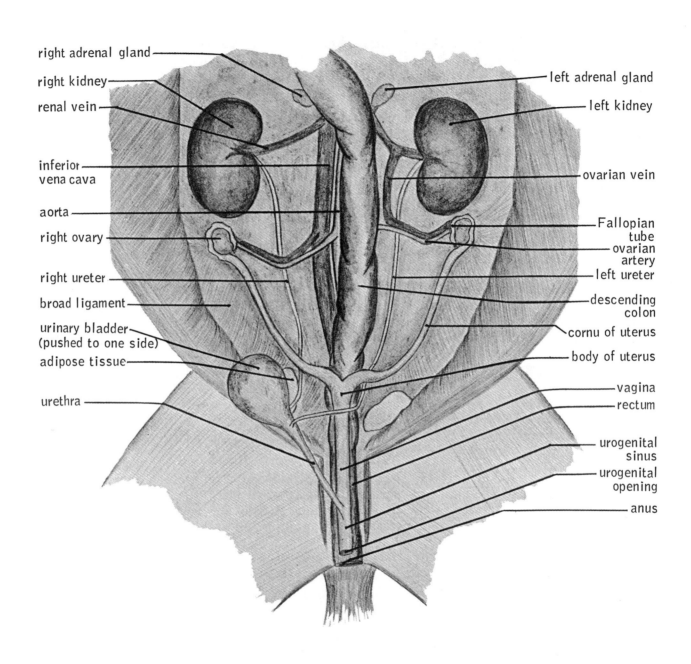

right adrenal gland

right kidney

renal vein

inferior vena cava

aorta

right ovary

right ureter

broad ligament

urinary bladder (pushed to one side)

adipose tissue

urethra

left adrenal gland

left kidney

ovarian vein

Fallopian tube

ovarian artery

left ureter

descending colon

cornu of uterus

body of uterus

vagina

rectum

urogenital sinus

urogenital opening

anus

Figure 40: Dissection of the Female Genitourinary System

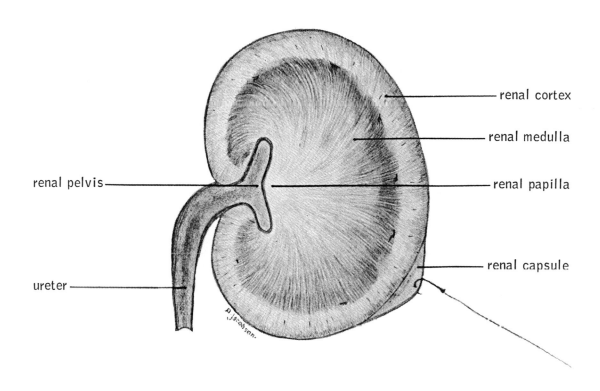

renal cortex

renal medulla

renal pelvis

renal papilla

renal capsule

ureter

Figure 41: Coronal Section through the Cat Kidney

c.   The next layer of the kidney, the renal medulla, contains one large dark renal pyramid.

d.   Locate the renal pelvis, the funnel-shaped expansion of the ureter inside the renal sinus, which is the hollow interior of the kidney. Identify the single renal papilla, the rounded projection of the pyramid of the medulla in the renal pelvis.

e.   Trace the renal artery into the kidney. Locate the interlobar, arcuate, and interlobular arteries. The corresponding veins should also be identified. (See Figure 43.)

10.   Compare the structure of the cat kidney with that of the human kidney (see Figures 42 and 43).

11.   Replace the kidney in the abdominal cavity of the cat.

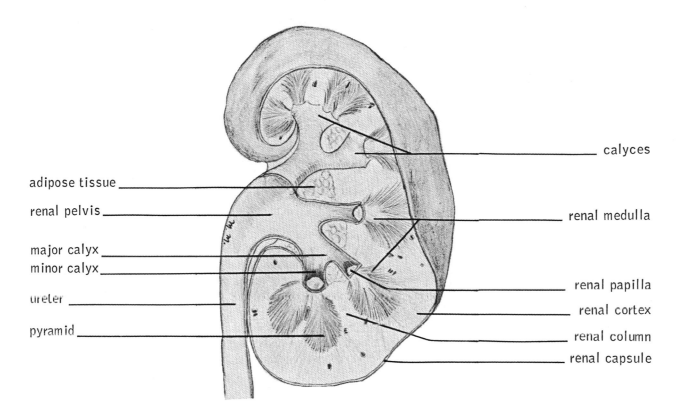

adipose tissue _____

renal pelvis _____

major calyx _____
minor calyx _____

ureter _____

pyramid _____

_____ calyces

_____ renal medulla

_____ renal papilla
_____ renal cortex
_____ renal column
_____ renal capsule

Figure 42: Longitudinal Section
through the Human Kidney

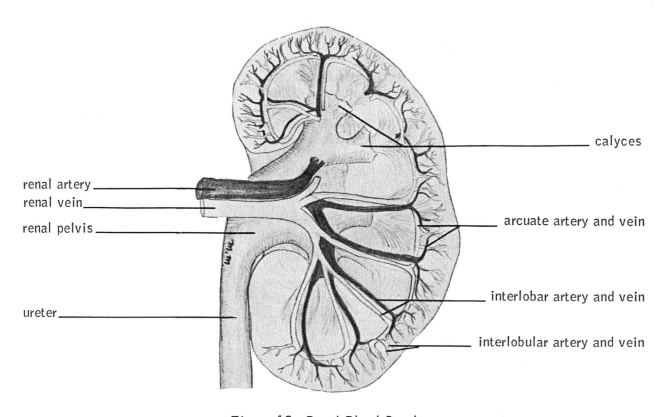

renal artery _____
renal vein _____

renal pelvis _____

ureter _____

_____ calyces

_____ arcuate artery and vein

_____ interlobar artery and vein

_____ interlobular artery and vein

Figure 43: Renal Blood Supply

Dissection of the Endocrine Glands

The important endocrine glands of the cat have been identified as they were located in the dissection of other organ systems. Therefore, this exercise will serve as a review of these glands.

PROCEDURE

1. Locate the thyroid glands in the neck region (see Figure 32). The two lobes of the thyroid lie one on each side of the anterior end of the trachea. The two lobes are connected by a narrow thin isthmus that is often destroyed in the dissection of the trachea.

2. Four tiny parathyroid glands are embedded in the dorsal surface of the thyroids. These are not visible with the unaided eye, however, due to their size.

3. The adrenal glands are located anterior and medial to each kidney (see Figure 40). Each gland resembles a small lymph node.

4. The pituitary gland (hypophysis) is located in the sella turcica of the sphenoid bone. It is attached to the hypothalamus by a stalk called the infundibulum. If you removed the brain of the cat, the pituitary can be seen in the floor of the cranial cavity in the sella turcica. It is not necessary to expose this gland if the brain was not removed.

5. The pineal gland may be observed in either the cat or sheep brain above the superior colliculi of the midbrain (see Figure 39).

6. The thymus gland as observed anterior and ventral to the heart (see Figure 32). This gland may have been removed with the pericardium.

7. The pancreas is located in the abdominal cavity between the duodenum and the spleen (see Figure 31).

8. The location of the ovaries and testes are described in the next section on the Reproductive System. (See Figure 40 for the location of the ovaries, and Figure 44 for the location of the testes in the cat.)

Dissection of the Reproductive System

The reproductive organs of the cat are similar to those of the human. Note, however, the differences in the structure of the uterus in the female and the absence of the seminal vesicle gland and ejaculatory duct in the male. Although you will dissect the reproductive system of only one sex, you are responsible for that of both sexes. Therefore, carefully study the reproductive structures on a cat of the opposite sex.

Part 1. The Female Reproductive System

PROCEDURES

1. Use Figure 40 as a guide in your dissection. Identify the ovaries, a pair of small light-colored oval bodies located posterior to the kidneys.

2. The uterine tubes (Fallopian tubes) are very small, highly convoluted tubes lying on the anterior surface of the ovaries. The expanded end (infundibulum) of the Fallopian tube partially covers the ovary and receives eggs (ova) through the opening (ostium) of the tube.

3. Trace the Fallopian tubes until a larger tube is reached immediately next to each ovary. These tubes, the uterine horns or cornua, are the beginning of the uterus. The eggs are carried through the Fallopian tubes to the uterine horns where they develop. The fetuses tend to be equally spaced throughout the two horns. The broad ligament supports the uterine horns and body of the uterus, extending from the cornua and body to the lateral body walls.

4. The two horns unite in the midline to form the body of the uterus which lies dorsal to the urethra.

5. To dissect the rest of the female reproductive system, the pelvic cavity must be exposed. Cut through the pelvic muscles and the pubic symphysis in the midventral line. Cut with care since the urethra lies immediately beneath the pubis. Open the area further by pushing back on the thighs to crack the bone.

6. Locate the urethra, the tube carrying urine from the urinary bladder.

7. Dorsal to the urethra, identify the vagina, the tube leading from the posterior end of the uterus.

8. Separate the urethra from the vagina. Toward the posterior end, the vagina and urethra unite to form a common passage which opens to the outside called the urogenital sinus or vestibule. The external opening is called the urogenital opening.

9. Examine the vulva, the external genitalia. The labia majora, the large lips surrounding the opening of the urogenital sinus, are visible.

10. Locate the rectum, the continuation of the large intestine, dorsal to the vagina.

Part 2. The Male Reproductive System

PROCEDURES

1.   Use Figure 44 as a guide in your dissection.   Locate the scrotum, the double sac ventral to the anus.   Early in fetal development, the testes are located below the kidneys; they migrate, however, before birth through the inguinal canal into the scrotum.   The scrotum is covered with skin on the outside and lined with peritoneum.   It is divided into two compartments by a median septum.

2.   Remove the skin from the scrotum.   Cut open the scrotum and examine the two testes.   They are oval bodies covered with peritoneum; this covering is called the tunica vaginalis.

3.   The epididymis should next be located along the anterior and lateral side of each testis.   This is a long coiled tube which receives sperm from the testis.   It begins at the cranial end of the gonad and extends to its caudal end.

4.   Locate the inguinal canals, two openings in the abdominal wall, by tracing the internal spermatic arteries posteriorly from the aorta until they pass through the inguinal canal.

5.   The vas deferens (ductus deferens) carries the sperm from the epididymis through the inguinal canal to empty into the urethra.   Trace the vas deferens as it passes along the ventral surface of the pelvis, accompanied by the testicular artery, vein, and nerve.   Collectively these structures, covered with connective tissue, are called the spermatic cord.   Follow the vas deferens through the inguinal canal to the urethra, noting how it loops over the ureter and enters the dorsal surface of the urethra.

6.   Locate the penis ventral to the scrotum. The glans penis is the enlargement at the distal end of the organ.   The opening to the outside is called the urogenital opening or aperture.   The prepuce or foreskin covers the glans penis.   Remove the overlying skin so that the penis is exposed.

7.   To dissect the rest of the male reproductive system, the pelvic cavity must be exposed.   Cut through the pelvic muscles and the pubic symphysis in the midventral line.   Cut with care since the urethra lies immediately beneath the pubis.   Open the area further by pushing back on the thighs to crack the bone.

8.   The urethra should now be visible emerging from the urinary bladder.   Trace this down to the penis.   Observe the opening of the vas deferens into the dorsal surface of the urethra.   Locate the prostate gland at the point where the vas deferens opens into the urethra.

9.   The urethra is divided into three parts: the prostatic urethra surrounded by the prostate gland; the membranous urethra between the prostate gland and the penis; and the spongy urethra, the part passing through the penis.

10.   Locate the two bulbourethral glands, one on either side of the membranous urethra.

11.   Observe the rectum dorsal to the urethra.

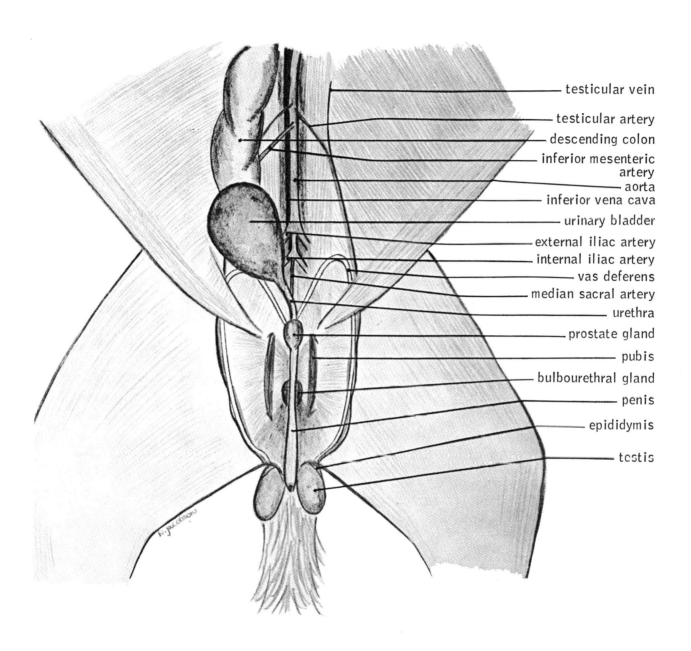

testicular vein

testicular artery

descending colon

inferior mesenteric
artery

aorta

inferior vena cava

urinary bladder

external iliac artery

internal iliac artery

vas deferens

median sacral artery

urethra

prostate gland

pubis

bulbourethral gland

penis

epididymis

testis

Figure 44: Reproductive System of the Male Cat